★ Young Man from the Piedmont ★

Young Man from the Piedmont

The Youth of Thomas Jefferson

LEONARD WIBBERLEY

Ariel Books · Farrar, Straus and Company · New York

★ Young Man from the Piedmont ★

1

Mr. Peter Jefferson was seated in a winged chair in the withdrawing room or parlor of his house, which was called Shadwell and lay east of the Rivanna River in the colony of Virginia. He was a big man and an active one, but a time had arrived in his life when no activity on his part was of any avail. He sat in the chair crouched over a little, thumping a clenched fist into the palm of his hand as if this motion would in some way help the outcome of the event which he awaited in distress. Now and again he would glance at a large clock which stood between two pieces of Venetian glassware on the mantelpiece over the fireplace. The clock had a loud strong tick which at other times was comforting. Now he found it irritating, and indeed foreboding. It was as if the clock might be ticking away someone's life, and he twice got up to stop the pendulum, and twice resisted this impulse.

From the bedroom at the back of the house he could hear now and again a suppressed groan. At the sound he would half rise from his chair with a look of desperation on his face. And then he would collapse into it and once again start pounding his big right fist into his left palm, glancing every now and again at the clock.

The year was 1743 and at the half-open door of the room was a Negro slave. His face was troubled and he kept his eyes on his master. Now and again he would mutter something as if he were talking to a third person, though there were only the two present. This was his way of talking to his master when he was in distress; without disrespect. He spoke to this third person and his master could overhear what was said and might be comforted.

"Seen two gray squirrels sitting on a pine branch," the Negro said. "Lawdy they was fat." He chuckled at the fatness of the squirrels. "John said for to go and get a gun and shoot them two squirrels for dinner, but I done said 'No sir. Not nothing a-going to be killed on Master's land this day when his son gonna be born. Not nothing going to be killed. Not even a little fly.

For this is a birthing day.' And them two squirrels they looked at me like they knowed all along they was safe and then went on chattering to each other."

Peter Jefferson made no sign that he had heard all this, and the slave, still studying his master, thought of something else that might be comforting.

"Down in them rich tidewater places they does say that all babies is born when the tide turns the river back—that is, all man babies. If a baby is born when the tide is running out and the river is flowing behind it, then likely it will be a girl. But if the baby comes when the tide is rushing in from the sea and piling up the river water and stopping it flowing down, then it will be a boy. That's because boys is strong like the sea is stronger than the river. But up here, that's all of no account. Ain't no tide ever reaches up here. But Blossom dropped her foal this very morning and it were a stallion—prettiest little thing you ever did see. And that's a sign if ever I did hear of a sign."

Peter Jefferson turned and looked at the slave and said with a wry smile, "It's been four and a half hours. Jane was seven hours and Mary six and a half . . ."

He was interrupted by a sharp cry from the bedroom. He got swiftly out of the chair and, pushing past the Negro, strode down the corridor to the door of the bedroom. Outside was a crowd of women houseslaves who made room for him, pushing each other back so that when he reached the door, he stood alone before it, the Negroes watching him from the lower end of the corridor. He stood irresolute for a moment, and then hearing nothing but labored breathing from the bedroom was about to put his hand on the latch when the door opened and the doctor stood before him, wiping his hands on a towel.

"A boy, Mr. Jefferson," he said briskly. "A boy. Weighs nine pounds, I'll warrant, and wonderfully strong . . ."

"My wife . . . ?" asked Peter Jefferson, looking over the doctor to the big bed on which she lay.

"All well," said the doctor. "A fine woman and a brave one. The pulse is good. You may see her for a minute, but she needs rest."

Peter Jefferson went over to the bed and stood towering over it for a minute. Then he knelt by the bedside and took his wife's hand in his. Her eyes were closed and she was very drowsy but she opened them for a moment and looked at her husband and said, "A boy . . . a son. . . ."

"Yes," he said. "Yes." That was all he could say, for his heart was too full with gratitude that his wife had survived the ordeal and had given birth to a son. He wanted to do something to help his wife, and noting that there was a little film of perspiration on her forehead, he took his handkerchief and gently patted her brow. Then, seeing that she seemed asleep, he got up, the wooden floor of the bedroom creaking under his huge weight, and said in a whisper to the doctor who stood behind him, "Where's the boy?"

The doctor gestured to a screened-off area of the

bedroom. "The women are attending to him," he said. "They'll bring him in a minute."

It was a little while before a middle-aged Negro woman came from behind the screen, carrying a bundled-up morsel of humanity.

"Gonna be big like the master," the woman said. "My goodness, but he's a long baby. And got a parcel of red hair. Never did see such red hair on a little ol' baby before." She laughed with delight at the thought of the red-haired baby, and Peter Jefferson took his son from her and pushed the blanket away from the little face.

"He looks worried," he said.

"They all looks worried," said the woman. "It's a worrisome business coming into the world all little and new."

Peter Jefferson walked out of the bedroom into the corridor where the rest of the household servants together with most of the field hands were gathered. They crowded around to see the baby, and Peter Jefferson turned to one of them. "Saddle a horse and ride to Tuckahoe and tell Mr. Randolph that I have a son," he said. "I'll give you a note to take to him. Be as quick as you can, for he will be anxious."

William Randolph, a member of one of the richest of the Virginia families, was Peter Jefferson's closest friend. They had made many trips into the wilderness together, hunting and surveying, and they had applied for and been granted several thousand acres of land up in the wilds along the Rivanna River, a tributary of the James. He should be the first to know of the birth of his friend's son.

William Randolph had a big plantation house at Tuckahoe, on the James River in Henrico County. But Peter Jefferson did not come of a wealthy family like the Randolphs and had to establish his own fortune, though he had inherited a large tract of land from his father. He had decided to build his family home, as a pioneer, on the virgin lands along the Rivanna but when he came to look over the area for a suitable site, he found that the best site was on land owned by his friend Randolph, on the eastern bank of the river.

"What would you take for two hundred acres of your land?" Peter asked his friend over a bowl of punch at the Randolph plantation at Tuckahoe.

"You like this punch?" asked William Randolph.

"Yes," said Peter, surprised, for punch didn't seem to have much to do with the matter.

"Well," said William with a twinkle in his eye, "it is a good arrack punch and I like it. It will cool you when you are hot, warm you when you are cold, and raise your spirits when you're depressed."

"Not a doubt about it," agreed Peter Jefferson, still mystified.

"Good. Then for the two hundred acres of my land, you must pay me the biggest bowl of arrack punch that is to be had from the Raleigh Tavern at Williamsburg," said Randolph. And that was the bargain agreed upon. Peter Jefferson got his two hundred acres of land for the bowl of punch, and bought another two hundred acres for fifty pounds. He married William Randolph's cousin Jane, and on the land acquired established his family home which he named Shadwell, after the parish in London, England, where Jane had been born. And now he had a son to carry on the Jefferson name. Life was good indeed.

When Peter Jefferson built his house, Shadwell, on the Rivanna River, six years before the birth of his eldest son whom he called Thomas, there were only two or three other settlers in the area. Virgin forest covered the land and there were but a few trails through it and those uncertain. People traveled on foot or on horseback and had often to dismount and hack their way through thickets. The area was known as the Piedmont country, meaning, "the country at the foot of the mountains." Westward the land rose in a series of mountain chains dominated by the Blue Ridge Mountains. They were forest-clad mountains thickly covered with magnificent growths of oak, beach, elm, and pine. The true frontier with its stockades and blockhouses lay only a hundred miles west of Shadwell.

But Peter Jefferson's house was not the little log cabin of the Kentucky pioneers. Using slave labor, he laid out good foundations of stone, enclosing cellars for storing food, and on these foundations built a large wooden house of four huge rooms. It was a story and a half high, the area enclosed by the roof being made into quarters for the household servants and bedrooms for the children.

Lower down the river, where the Rivanna and the Fluvanna joined to form the James, lay what was called the Tidewater country. Here was a coastal plain of rich alluvial land, stretching a hundred miles to the sea. William Randolph's plantation, Tuckahoe, lay in the Tidewater country, so called because, twice in every twenty hours, the incoming tide from the Chesapeake Bay reversed the flow of the James River, raising its level until it lapped and sometimes overflowed the rim of its banks.

This sea tide was of the greatest benefit to the tobacco planters of the Tidewater area. It allowed ships to come up the river and tie up to wharves at the foot of their plantations. Onto the ships slaves loaded big hogsheads of tobacco weighing a thousand pounds apiece for shipment to England. Tobacco was the golden crop of Virginia—the whole source of wealth of the country. It was so valuable that it was used instead of money for paying debts and it was more certain of retaining its value than money.

There was a shortage of English currency in Virginia and through most of the southern colonies attempts to establish a colonial currency failed, for people did not trust the colonial money. But they trusted tobacco. That could always be relied upon to fetch a good price in England, where it was exchanged for goods or entered as credit on the books of London and Bristol merchants.

The great families of Virginia lived in luxury on the

Tidewater, made rich by their golden tobacco crops worked by their slaves.

Life was harder in the Piedmont where Thomas Jefferson was born. Land had still to be cleared before it could be planted with tobacco and corn. Travel was difficult. Men had still to work with their hands, master and slave at times laboring together. In some areas the climate or soil was unsuited to tobacco and less profitable crops were raised. What tobacco was cultivated had to be rolled in stout hogsheads along trails to the Tidewater for shipment, or a dozen hogsheads might be put on board two canoes lashed together and taken down the shallow Rivanna to the deeper waters of the James.

The Tidewater planters were the ruling class, fully represented in the House of Burgesses where, all being to their satisfaction, they resisted change. The planters of the Piedmont had not so much say in the House of Burgesses, and wanted more.

Peter Jefferson, living in the Piedmont and related to the wealthy Randolphs of the Tidewater, was acquainted with the highest and the lowest classes of people in Virginia. He had had little schooling, being taught to read and write by his father, but had a passion for knowledge, and spent many an evening learning mathematics so that his services were in demand as a surveyor.

He added to his profits from his pioneer plantation by undertaking surveys for the royal governor. He loved the wilderness, and with Joshua Fry, professor of mathematics at the College of William and Mary in Williamsburg, he surveyed the boundary line between Virginia and North Carolina. One of the first maps of Virginia was made by Peter Jefferson and Joshua Fry. He not only knew the Scots and Irish frontiersmen of the wilderness, but also the Indians who hunted and lived in the Blue Ridge and Appalachian Mountains. These were his friends, and whenever a party of them were on their way to Williamsburg, there to petition the governor for some favor, they always stopped at his house, camping on the grounds of his plantation. They made a trail out of the mountains past Shadwell and it was not unusual for a hundred Cherokees to pitch their tents on the rough pasturage around Peter Jefferson's big house.

On this plantation there was a little mountain, almost denuded of trees, and from its peak it was possible, looking westward, to see the line of the forested Blue Ridge Mountains forming a barrier against the sky. When Tom Jefferson was old enough his father often took him to the top of this little mountain to see the view. Wave after wave of mountain range rose blue in the evening sky as far as the eye could see. Sometimes hosts of carrier pigeons fluttered in dark ragged streamers across the tops of the forests. In the still of the evening the boy could hear the gobbling of wild turkeys in the underbrush, the eerie, snarling cry of a hunting bobcat, or the crashing of a startled deer through the thicket. Tom Jefferson as a boy never tired of the sights and sounds to be enjoyed from the top of this little mountain which lay on the other side of the Rivanna River from Shadwell.

"What lies beyond the mountains?" he asked his father.

"More mountains."

"And beyond them?"

"A big river—the Mississippi."

"And beyond the river?"

Peter Jefferson shrugged. "Nobody knows for sure, except maybe the Spanish. Some say a desert and some say grassland. The Indians say both."

"Who owns the land there?"

"The Spanish claim to own it."

"Well, beyond the Spanish land, what else is there?"

"I don't know, son," said Peter Jefferson. "But thousands of miles away there is another ocean—the Pacific. And beyond that is China."

"But nobody really knows what lies beyond the Mississippi?"

"No. It's not mapped. There are stories of people who went into that land. But we haven't any records."

The boy looked at the blue mountains and thought of the big river miles and miles beyond them, and beyond the river hundreds of miles of land that nobody knew anything about. It was something to dream about; and climbing to the top of the little mountain that he was later to call Monticello, he dreamed about it often.

☆ ☆ ☆ ☆ ☆ ☆ ☆ ☆ ☆ ☆ ☆

2

When Thomas Jefferson was two years old, his father's best friend, William Randolph, died. His death was completely unexpected. He was only thirty-three years old and the blow lay heavily on his family, for his wife had died only a short while before. His three daughters, Judith, Mary, and Priscilla, and his four-year-old son Thomas Mann Randolph, were left orphans.

A messenger on a sweat-soaked horse brought the news to Peter Jefferson, seventy miles away at Shadwell. Peter Jefferson didn't hesitate over what to do. He had promised his friend that if he died he would take care of his children and his plantation. He appointed an overseer for his own estates, got together his baggage and a few slaves, and set out with his family for Tuckahoe. By now Peter Jefferson had another child, a daughter, Elizabeth, who was only six months old. The family traveled by horseback through the wilderness. No coach or carriage could get through the narrow trails over the mountains. Two-year-old Thomas Jefferson was placed on a pillow on the saddle croup of one of the slaves. Peter Jefferson carried his infant daughter Elizabeth in his arms. The journey took three days, and at night they camped out in the forest, the father, who was used to the outdoor life, putting up tents with the help of the slaves.

The elder girls thought it was great fun. They helped to look after the baby, and Jane was given the job of seeing that little Tom didn't toddle off into the woods and get lost. She loved him dearly because he was the only boy in the family; she changed his clothes, washed and fed him, and slept beside him during the night. The slaves teased her and called her "little mother."

Tuckahoe, the Randolph plantation house, was a mansion compared with Shadwell. It was built in the form of an H, being actually two two-story houses connected by a large hallway or salon, which was so big that it readily held four sofas and several chairs, and was lighted by an enormous chandelier suspended from the high ceiling. This salon served for entertainments—for lavish dinners or balls, for during his lifetime William Randolph had been fond of company and delighted in giving big dinners and dances to which he invited guests from forty or fifty miles around. The guests were not expected to return to their homes after the dinner or the dance. They were accommodated in one of the two houses making up the Tuckahoe mansion, and often stayed as long as a week, riding, hunting and fishing, with dancing each evening before returning to their homes.

Mrs. Peter Jefferson knew the house well, for she had often been there during her childhood. It was no great problem for her, with plenty of servants, to take care of the mixed family of eight children—half of them Randolphs and half her own. Peter Jefferson was the one with the problem, for he now had two estates to manage—Tuckahoe and his own plantation seventy miles up the river.

But he was a man of great energy and a methodical man as well. Nothing was done on either of the estates without his direction and knowledge. He kept separate account books for the two of them, scrupulously noting the purchase of a mare or the payment of a blacksmith. He personally superintended the loading of the hogsheads of tobacco on the ships docked on the James River at the foot of the huge lawn before the plantation house. Once, seeing some men struggling to stand one of the heavy hogsheads on end, he told them to move aside and got between two of the great barrels. He bent down and put his big hands on the rims of the barrels and upended the two of them at the same time—handling with the enormous strength of his back and shoulders something like a ton of weight.

Soon Peter Jefferson had matters so well organized that he was able to go off surveying again. His children grew accustomed to not seeing their father for weeks and sometimes months, between his surveying and his visits to the Shadwell estate. But they lived happily in the splendid Tuckahoe mansion, and when he was home Peter Jefferson would give dinner parties and dances.

He hired a tutor to teach the girls to dance and he danced with them, the huge man carefully performing the figures of a minuet with solemn little girls of nine and ten. He saw to it that the boys, when they were old enough, learned to dance too, for he believed a gentleman should be as apt on the dance floor as on the back of a horse.

There was, on the Tuckahoe estate, a little schoolhouse, built of boards and of but one room. Here, the children were sent every day to "English school" under a private tutor. Jane led her little brother Thomas weeping to the schoolhouse when he was five years of age to start his lessons. He struggled with the alphabet and the multiplication tables, recited by the children aloud in a singsong voice. He learned first to print letters and then to write in Spencer's script. And when he had learned to write his own name, he wrote it proudly, while Jane watched, on the walls of the school, and it is still there to this day.

His sister Jane helped him all the time. She rehearsed him in the tricky difference between "m" and "n" and checked over his sums, done painfully on a slate. She went fishing with him but let Tom put the worms on the hook, and when, playing by the river, he got his shoes wet, she conspired with the kitchen slaves to dry them by the fire so he wouldn't get into trouble.

Thomas Jefferson had four years of schooling at Tuckahoe, and then the family returned to their own home at Shadwell, arrangements being made for the care of the Randolph children.

Back at Shadwell, Peter Jefferson wondered whether the pampered life at Tuckahoe and the company of so many girls had not softened his young son Thomas. The boy was nine years of age, tall, slender, but with good bones and strong.

"When I was your age," Peter told him, "I was a pretty good shot. I used to borrow my father's gun and go out and shoot some game in the woods for dinner."

Tom considered this for a moment. "May I borrow your gun, sir?" he asked, blushing a little.

"Certainly," said his father. "You'll find powder horn and shot right by it." He grinned. "Do you think you'll get a turkey?"

"I won't come home without one," said Tom Jefferson.

The next morning he was up early and off into the woods. He spent the whole day there but he hadn't the knack of a woodland hunter. He was too clumsy in moving about and not quick enough with his gun, and though he saw several turkeys and shot at them, they fluttered off unhurt, mocking him with their gobbling. Late in the afternoon Tom started back empty-handed, ashamed and at the same time angry with himself that he had missed with every ball he fired. When he was about half a mile from Shadwell, he heard a turkey clucking in the underbrush nearby. He crept forward cautiously toward the sound, peeked over the top of some low-growing dogwood, and saw the turkey. It was a wild turkey, all right, but it was in a wooden pen. Someone had caught it as a chick and decided to raise it to provide a meal later on.

Tom thought the situation over for a moment. He had said he wouldn't come back without a turkey and here was one right before him. On the other hand, he couldn't shoot it there in the pen. But again, if he let it out of the pen, it would certainly fly off before he could get a shot at it.

He undid one of his garters, grabbed the turkey, and tied it by a leg to a sapling. Then he backed off what he thought was a fair distance, took aim and fired. The turkey fell dead on the ground and Tom picked it up and carried it back to Shadwell.

"Did you shoot it yourself?" Peter Jefferson asked.

"Yes sir," said Tom.

★ 19 ★

"Hm'm," said his father. "Well it seems as though you are a better woodsman than I took you for. We shall have it for dinner tomorrow."

Tom never told his father the true story of that turkey. But he told Jane, for he had no secrets from her. "It wasn't quite honest," he said, "but all I said was that I'd bring back a turkey."

"I think it's very clever," said Jane adoringly. "Will you teach me to shoot sometime?"

"Sure," said Tom. "It's very easy, really. The only thing is, don't close your eyes when you pull the trigger."

"It would be so nice to be a boy," said Jane wistfully.

They were as inseparable at Shadwell as they were at Tuckahoe. They went together to the Indian camps when the Cherokee came by down the river on their way to Williamsburg, and the Indians taught them how to handle a canoe. Peter Jefferson made a canoe for Tom and he and Jane made trips up and down the river in it, pretending to be explorers of the mysterious Mississippi.

"Nobody really knows where it comes from," said Tom. "There are other big rivers flowing into it and nobody has ever been up them to find out what kind of land is there. But some day I'm going to find out."

"Will you take me with you?" asked Jane.

"You'll be married by then," said Tom.

"I suppose so," said Jane a little sadly. Then she

brightened, "If I'm not married, will you take me with you?"

"Certainly."

"Tom. Let's never be separated. Let's be together all the time."

Tom considered this gravely. "We'll have to be separated sometime," he said. "That's the way it is when you grow up. You'll live in one place and I'll live in another. But I won't ever forget you, Jane."

"And I won't forget you," said Jane. "Never. And if you're sick you're to send for me."

They were separated earlier than they expected. There was no school at Shadwell or near Shadwell and Peter Jefferson was not satisfied with the amount of education Tom had. He read well and liked reading, even borrowing volumes of *The Spectator* from his father's library to read the essays of Steele and Addison. He read books like *Travels Into Several Remote Nations of the World,* by a man called Lemuel Gulliver who, his father said, was really Jonathan Swift, a brilliant clergyman of Dublin, Ireland.

But Tom Jefferson had no knowledge of Latin or Greek and so all the classics were closed to him except in translation. And furthermore his mathematics was limited to arithmetic, without even a touch of algebra or geometry. Peter Jefferson, casting around for a school for his son, was delighted to learn that the Reverend William Douglas, recently arrived from Scotland, had undertaken to open a school to teach classics and mathematics, to young ladies and gentlemen. His school would be at Dover Creek, near Tuckahoe, and Peter Jefferson arranged to pay the Reverend Mr. Douglas nineteen pounds sterling a year to educate his son.

That was the end of the brief happy days with Jane at Shadwell. Thomas Jefferson went to Dover Creek to be tutored by Mr. Douglas for the next five years.

Mr. Douglas was not the Latin scholar that Peter Jefferson took him for. He did teach young Tom the rudiments of Latin and Greek, leading him through the simpler declensions and conjugations, but Virgil and Cato and Homer strained his powers. Thomas Jefferson spent hours translating into Latin and Greek sentences like "The girls crown the queen with roses," and then "The girls *will* crown the queen with roses," and then "The girls *have crowned* the queen with roses." But he got hardly a peek at Homer's *Iliad* and Virgil's *Aeneid*.

He did, however, learn French, for Mr. Douglas was proficient in that language and fond of tracing French words to their Latin roots. He might misspell a few Latin endings here and there but his French was correct, and at the end of five years' study, fourteen-year-old Thomas Jefferson was fluent in French and not entirely at a loss with Latin and Greek.

He had furthermore developed a keen interest in languages so that he soon undertook the study of Italian on his own—aided by Mr. Douglas' tussles with Latin. Then he ventured into German, but never mastered this language, for Anglo-Saxon, the language from which English developed, claimed his attention.

Five years, then, Thomas Jefferson spent at the Douglas school, boarded by the clergyman who was so careful with his money that he served the same meat pie day after day until it was moldy. Tom worked hard and went to Shadwell during holidays or visited the Randolphs at nearby Tuckahoe.

Then came a big change. In late June of 1757, Peter Jefferson, who was then only forty-nine years of age, fell ill. He was ill enough to have to go to bed and Thomas Walker, his friend and doctor, visited him. Dr. Walker called three times to see Peter Jefferson in July but his patient did not improve. In August, the doctor made almost daily calls. On the seventeenth of August, Peter Jefferson died.

At the age of fourteen Tom Jefferson became the head of his family. There were now seven other children, the youngest a boy of two named Randolph.

His boyhood had ended. He must succeed his father and become a man.

☆ ☆ ☆ ☆ ☆ ☆ ☆ ☆ ☆ ☆ ☆

3

Standing in the large living room of Shadwell, the attorney adjusted his small wire-rimmed glasses and, with a sympathetic nod toward Mrs. Peter Jefferson, recently widowed, started to read the will of Peter Jefferson. To fourteen-year-old Thomas Jefferson, seated on a sofa close to his sister Jane, the whole procedure seemed utterly unreal. His father's life was being laid out before him in a statement of the possessions he had acquired, the possessions listed by the lawyer in a dry voice devoid of any emotion, and punctuated by an occasional little cough. When the lawyer uttered this little cough, he was careful first of all to produce a linen handkerchief which he put before his thin mouth, as if all coughs without the benefit of this handkerchief were illegal and should be stricken from the record.

Tom had no idea that his father had amassed so much wealth in his short life. He was accustomed to the splendor of the Tuckahoe mansion, the richness and vastness of the grounds around, the magnificent lace tablecloths, the plentitude of Queen Anne silverware, and the abundance of slaves.

Shadwell did not compare with Tuckahoe. Yet it seemed as the will proceeded that his father must have amassed wealth at least equal to that possessed by the Randolphs. Some of the wealth Peter Jefferson had inherited from his own father, in particular an estate at Snowdon lower down the river. But most of it Peter Jefferson had created himself with his enormous energy. The will then was for Tom a kind of summary of his father's life, and made the grief of his loss heavier to bear. He had not known his father had worked so hard and to such purpose.

There were nearly three thousand acres of the estate at Shadwell. These were willed to Mrs. Jefferson for the rest of her life together with one-sixth of the slaves and all the household articles. There were other parcels of lands on the Rivanna, Fluvanna, and Hardware rivers which were divided between Tom and his infant brother Randolph. A number of the slaves were to be divided among the six daughters (together with their natural increase) and each of the daughters was to get two hundred pounds as a marriage portion or payable to them when they reached the age of twenty-one if they did not marry. There was a special clause directed to Tom, and when the attorney came to it, he removed his glasses and gave his little cough, producing the handkerchief as license, and looked over at the fourteen-year-old boy for a few minutes until all in the room turned to look at him also. The attorney then replaced his glasses and continued with his reading:

"I give and bequeath to my son Thomas my mulatto fellow Tawney, my books, mathematical instruments and my cherry tree desk and bookcase. . . . I give and bequeath all my slaves not herein otherwise disposed of, to be equally divided between my two sons, Thomas and Randolph . . ." For a moment it seemed to Thomas Jefferson that his father was alive and had spoken directly to him. The gift of his cherry tree desk and his books and bookcase and mathematical instruments—that brought his father back to life. How often he had seen his father working at that desk in the evening. Many mornings he had gone into his father's study and seen on the desk two candles burned almost to stubs—evidence of how late his father had worked. The desk was his now, to work at as his father had done.

Under the will four guardians were appointed to administer the estate until Thomas came of age. They were Peter Randolph, a cousin of his mother's; Thomas Turpin, Thomas' uncle; Dr. Thomas Walker; and John Harvie—all old friends and business associates of Peter Jefferson.

When the reading of the will was finished, refreshments were served and while the attorney was discreetly congratulating Mrs. Jefferson on the excellent manner in which her husband had managed his affairs "against that event which none may avoid," Thomas Jefferson slipped outside the house to get a breath of air. Before the house was a lawn divided by a driveway, and standing on the driveway were several Negroes holding the horses of the lawyer and the four guardians who had also attended the reading of the will.

"Master Tom," said one of them, "begging your pardon, but who do I belong to now?"

"To the Mistress," said Tom, surprised at the question.

The man gave a sigh of relief. Then he looked troubled again. "And Sarah Josephine, my wife . . . and the three children?"

"Why, to the Mistress too," said Tom.

The man grinned and the other slaves looked a little happier. "Ain't none of us going to be sold, is there, Master Tom?" one of them asked. "Master Peter left enough money so none of us has to be sold?"

"Of course he did," said Tom. "None of you will be sold. You'll stay here and be looked after as always."
Tom looked the men over. For the first time in his

life, the appalling situation of the slave, a human being who was a piece of property, came forcefully to
him. He knew every one of them. They were humans
like himself. But they had no rights—they were like
houses or furniture or parcels of land, to be disposed
of as their owner thought fit. Was it right to buy or sell
another human being? There seemed suddenly something wrong with that. Everybody did it. Everybody
he knew owned slaves. Even he himself owned slaves
now. The mulatto Tawney had been given to him
specifically by his father, as his father had given him
his cherrywood desk and his mathematical instruments.

If it were wrong to own slaves, shouldn't he set
Tawney free? But supposing he did free Tawney, what
would the ex-slave do for a living? Nobody would em-
ploy him. Nobody would pay him wages when they
could get all the work they wanted done by their
slaves for nothing. If he freed all the slaves that came
to him, then he would have to pay for labor on his
plantation. That would put the cost of his produce up
so high compared with plantations worked by slaves
that he would soon be bankrupt.

The question was a difficult one and he put it aside
to think about it later. But it was constantly in his
mind in the months ahead. Something had to be done
about slavery—but what? He did not know the answer.

Just before his father's death, Tom had left the
Reverend William Douglas' school to study under an-

other Scotsman, the Reverend James Maury. The Reverend Maury lived fourteen miles from Shadwell at the foot of Peter's Mountain. He was a much more learned man than the Reverend Douglas—a master of the classics and something more besides, for he was an amateur geologist and naturalist. He taught Latin, Greek, French, Philosophy, and History, and he mixed in with these field trips to look for fossils, or collect plants, or identify and count the birds and animals in the forests around.

He once showed young Tom a piece of fossilized clay he had found on Peter's Mountain with the imprint of a shell in it, and theorized that at one time the mountain had been at the bottom of an enormous sea. The Reverend Maury was a liberal in his thought —adhering blindly to no dogma—but demanding that each problem be examined and decided on its merits.

"Man was given reason to reason with," he told Tom. "Do not submit your reason to other men's prejudices. Examine everything for yourself, putting emotions aside. Then you are most likely to come to the correct conclusion."

They talked about theories of government— whether people were capable of governing themselves or whether it was necessary to have over them others of superior education who could handle affairs for them. Tom early inclined to the view that all men should have a say in how they were governed. The Reverend Maury posed the question of property. "If a man owns ten thousand pounds in property, hasn't he a right to a larger say in government than a man who owns only the clothes on his back? Wouldn't the one be inclined to be more responsible and the other less responsible?"

Tom hadn't a ready answer for that. His reason told him that someone with a big stake in a country, a city or a nation, was likely to be more prudent in handling its affairs than someone who had no such stake. But men were surely equal in that they had equal rights. One of those rights must be an equal influence in government affairs. Like slavery, this was a question to be examined deeply and over a long period.

Life at Mr. Maury's school wasn't all geology, philosophy, and classical studies. Tom Jefferson now owned his own horses and loved riding. He became one of the boldest riders in the neighborhood, saddling horses that others feared, riding the twelve miles from St. Peter's Mountain to Shadwell as often as he could to see his family and especially Jane.

After the fiasco of his first turkey hunt, he learned to shoot well, hunting deer and squirrels. There were three kinds of squirrels in the region—red, gray, and black. He took to weighing those he shot, keeping records of the weights and speculating on why there was a distinct weight difference between the different species. He made daily records of the temperature, noted the migrations of birds, kept records of wildflowers, specifying the kinds to be found and in what places and when they bloomed and so on. Everything he saw interested him, and when his sister Jane started taking music lessons, he took them too. Music entranced him. He decided to learn to play the violin, and practiced carefully every day for two or three hours. He found he had his father's energy, for he could put in fourteen hours of study a day.

"It is surprising how much you can do if you are always busy," he said once to his friend Dabney Carr, a fellow student under the Reverend Maury and the same age as himself. The two of them made a habit of studying together under a huge oak tree near Shadwell during vacations or on week-ends. They loved that oak tree which, filtering the sunlight, created a lovely constantly moving pattern of light and shadow on the ground.

"I'd like to be buried under this tree when I die," Tom said one day. He laughed. "It's a silly thing to say because when you are dead it doesn't really matter where you are buried. You can't know anything about it."

"I'd like to be buried under it too," said Dabney. "Listen, whoever of us dies first, let's promise that the other will bury him under this tree." They made the promise with all the intensity of young friends.

Under the same tree they discussed what they would do when they grew up.

"I'm going to study law," said Dabney Carr.

"At William and Mary?" Tom asked.

"Where else? Dr. Maury can't teach us law."

"Us?"

"Well, you'll study with me too, won't you?"

"I don't know whether I could get my guardians to consent to my going to William and Mary," said Tom.

"You can try," said Dabney. "You can't spend all your time studying with Dr. Maury."

That Christmas Tom spent two weeks as a guest of Colonel Dandridge, who had been a friend of his father's and kept a lavish house on his plantation in Hanover County on the South Anna River west of Shadwell. There were parties every night, for Colonel Dandridge kept open house for his neighbors during the holiday season. There were singing and dancing and amateur theatricals, and whoever could play a musical instrument was expected to do so for his fellow guests.

The merriest musician of them all was a tall, dark-haired, long-nosed, long-jawed young man named Patrick Henry. His coat, being a little old, fitted him tightly across the shoulders and his linen was not well pressed. He looked a bit of a ruffian among the other elegant guests and he had a peculiar accent, saying "nateral" for "natural" and "consarn" for "concern." He spent the days riding and hunting, always out with the men, and the evenings cracking jokes which were always funny but not always polite. He could play any kind of jig or reel on the fiddle and played for hours, refreshing himself with wine which he did not sip for the flavor but gulped down with great relish.

Tom was fascinated by Patrick Henry. The ladies clustered around him and the gentlemen too. He had a quip on every subject and gave an imitation of the London fashion in taking snuff that had everybody in stitches.

"Closed down my store," said Henry, "or it closed me down. I'll tell you how it was—there was a quarrel between me and bookkeeping and bookkeeping won. I'd want a pound to bet on a race and the books would say I couldn't have one. Well, they were my books so I took the pound anyway and be hanged to them. But they won in the end for there came a day when there wasn't a pound to be had.

"Then there was a thing called 'Accounts Receivable.' Never have anything to do with them. That's never-never money. It's money that you may receive if the feller that owes it to you comes into more money than he expects—and doesn't spend it before he gets around to paying you."

"What are you going to do now, Mr. Henry?" asked Tom.

"I'm going to read for the law, Mr. Jefferson," said Henry. "I'll be a lawyer. And when I'm a lawyer I'll never keep any books. Payment in advance or they can go without my sarvices. That's the way it will be with Patrick Henry."

"Will you go to Williamsburg to study?"

"I will," said Henry. And then he laughed. "For as short a time as possible," he added. "The law's just common sense. A man has his 'nateral' rights and that's all there is to it. Some statute passed during the reign of Henry III of England can't interfere with a man's 'nateral' rights."

"I may see you there," said Tom.

"You're going to college?"

"Well—" said Tom hesitatingly. "I'll have to ask my guardians."

"To be sure," said Mr. Henry. "To be sure." But he said it in such a way as to indicate that, if it were himself, he would go to college first and ask his guardians afterward. There was a touch of the buccaneer about Patrick Henry—a dashing, laughing audacity, a lively humor and a quick tongue.

After the Christmas at Dandridge's plantation, Tom returned to Shadwell but stopped first at the plantation of Colonel Peter Randolph, one of the Randolph clan who had been appointed one of his guardians.

They talked of Tom's future and his education. "You must mix about in the world, young man," said the Colonel. "Make friends, discuss affairs, get into a little trouble, maybe, and out of it. How old are you now?"

"Nearly seventeen . . ."

"Hmmm. It's time to be up and doing, my boy; getting ready to play a man's part in the world. You need to meet more people than come your way at Shadwell. Depend upon it—the friends you make in your youth will be of the greatest value for the remainder of your life. For my part, I think you ought to go to William and Mary College but you must secure the permission of your other guardians as well."

The most important of these was John Harvie, who had worked closely in many land deals with Tom's father and who now managed the business affairs of the Jeffersons. He was a man of plain sense, well read, and little ruled by his emotions. Tom knew he would have to advance some good reasons for wanting to go to college if John Harvie's agreement to the project was to be obtained.

Back at Shadwell, Tom composed several drafts of a letter to John Harvie before he felt he had the right version. The letter he sent was as follows:

"Sir: I was at Colonel Peter Randolph's about a fortnight ago & my schooling falling into Discourse, he said he thought it would be to my advantage to go to college, & was desirous I should go, as indeed I am myself for several reasons. In the first place as long as I stay at the Mountains the Loss of one fourth of my Time is inevitable, by company's coming here & detaining me from school. And likewise my Absence will in a great Measure put a stop to so much Company, & by that Means lessen the expenses of the Estate in house-keeping. And on the Other Hand by going to the College I shall get more universal Acquaintance, which may hereafter be serviceable to me; & I suppose I can pursue my

Studies in the Greek & Latin as well there as here, & likewise learn something of the Mathematics. I shall be glad of your opinion. . . ."

He believed that the arguments about not wasting so much time and reducing the expenses of the household would appeal to the business-like Mr. Harvie. He was right. In a few days came a reply giving his consent to Tom's attending William and Mary College in Williamsburg. Tom packed his books, said good-bye to his mother, to Jane and the rest of his family, saddled a horse and set off.

He had never been to a town in his life—never seen two houses that stood side by side, let alone a whole row of houses; never seen a shop nor attended a play other than amateur family theatricals. This was going to be a big adventure for him.

4

At first meeting, Williamsburg all but swallowed young Tom Jefferson. The town contained only two hundred houses and there were scarcely a thousand people living in it, including slaves. But it was still a far bigger place than Tom had ever seen, and it was as lively as New York or Boston or Philadelphia and perhaps even livelier. For one thing, it was the resort of the planters of Virginia who came to Williamsburg whenever the House of Burgesses was in session. They came officially to attend to public business as delegates to the

House. But they were all men of great wealth and blood and devoted to entertainment. And so they had, almost daily, horse racing or cock fighting, or dancing or hunting, or card playing bouts when hundreds of pounds exchanged hands on the turn of a card at the gambling tables.

So much money was spent in Williamsburg when the House of Burgesses was in session that theatrical companies from London crossed the Atlantic to stage the plays of Congreve and Shakespeare in the little town. A man would buy out the whole accommodation of the theater to invite his friends to a performance. Actors and actresses mixed gaily with the gentlemen of wealth who loved to parade through the streets in coaches drawn by three pairs of matched horses, with two wigged footmen standing on the back step of the coach.

Tom Jefferson, wealthy and of a good family, was welcomed at any event staged in anyone's house in Williamsburg. He was a good dancer and fond of dancing. He was a good rider and fond of riding. He found credit readily extended to him at the Raleigh Tavern or wherever he might have need of money. The shops of Williamsburg were willing to let him have what goods he wanted merely on his signature. And spending that would have struck him as folly at Shadwell began to appear utterly normal in Williamsburg, for the visiting gentry commonly spent heavily on clothes, horses, and entertainment.

In contrast with the excitement of the town, the

College of William and Mary was the dullest kind of place. The building itself had a gloomy prison look and on his first glimpse of it, Tom decided that, but for the roof, it looked like a brick kiln—a mere piling of bricks one upon the other without any attempt at grace or proportion. There were something less than a hundred students at the college. All were of the best families of Virginia and in the care of six masters. But the six masters were divided among four schools—a grammar school for boys under fifteen, a school of philosophy which was the college proper, a school of divinity for postgraduate students, and an Indian school. The latter was an attempt to educate Indians in English, but few Indians attended for long, or benefited much from the instruction.

Tom entered the school of philosophy but soon found the standards of his fellow students so below his own that he was quickly bored. He heard lectures on matters he had already mastered himself, and between this and the attractions of the town, he didn't do very much work in his first year at William and Mary. What brought him to his senses was first the bills he had run up by the end of the year, and second, the appointment of Dr. William Small of Scotland as head of the School of Philosophy.

His bills were very high—or so they seemed to Tom. There were bills for clothing, for he found his country dress outlandish in fashionable Williamsburg, and there were bills for horses. Every Virginia gentleman needed two or three good animals and Tom didn't want to be different, and he loved horses anyway. He was so overcome by remorse when he saw how much he had spent in his first year at Williamsburg that he wrote to John Harvie, his guardian, plainly stating that he had been extravagant and asking that the bills be paid out of his own portion of the estate, for it would not be fair to deduct the money from the general estate which would one day be divided between his sisters and his brother.

Harvie looked over the bills and the letter and chuckled. For a young man on his own for the first time, and in as gay a place as Williamsburg, the bills were by no means high. He wrote to Tom saying, "If you have sowed your wild oats in this way, the estate can well afford to pay the bill." The point was—had he finished sowing his wild oats? That was something for Tom to decide himself. Dr. William Small helped him to make the decision.

Dr. Small was one of the most learned men in Virginia. He liked the tall handsome red-headed Jefferson boy. When lectures were over and Tom was likely to head for town to see what was stirring, William Small would suggest a walk to stretch their legs and get some fresh air. Tom would hesitate. He had perhaps half promised to meet a fellow student at the Raleigh, or turn up at some wrestling match or horse race. Dr. Small would smile. He had been a student himself and knew these temptations.

"Come, Mr. Jefferson," he would say, "a man of your intelligence should have no difficulty choosing between the company of the Greek philosophers and the outcome of a horse race. There will always be horse races, Mr. Jefferson. They have been going on since the horse was first domesticated, but I do not know that the sum total of all the horse races that have ever been run has added one iota to the advancement of Man."

Such arguments appealed to Tom Jefferson. Dr. Small had a mind like an encyclopedia. He could discuss any question and with authority. Nor was his mind closed to new knowledge. He searched for it as if it were a treasure, and finding Tom Jefferson eager for learning and able to hold up his end in an argument, he had soon introduced him to Francis Fauquier, Governor of Virginia, and one of the most accomplished men ever to hold that position.

It was typical of the eighteenth century that Francis Fauquier owed his position as Governor of Virginia to the fact that he had lost his whole fortune in one night's gambling in London.

He was the son of a director of the Bank of England, and on his father's death, heir to enormous wealth. He was an outstanding economist and had written a treatise opposing the piling up of a national debt. He proposed that governments should tax the income of their subjects to meet expenses, instead of borrowing money which had to be repaid at heavy interest. In proposing a tax on income, Francis Fauquier was a good century ahead of his times. He was handsome and polished, extremely interested in music and literature, had exquisite manners—and an abiding love of gambling.

Shortly after the famous Admiral Anson returned from his voyage around the world, he met Francis Fauquier in London and the two were soon engaged in a game of backgammon. The stakes got higher and higher and when the last hand had been played Fauquier had lost to Admiral Anson the whole fortune he had inherited from his father.

Too much of the gentleman to complain, Fauquier thanked the Admiral for his night's sport and went to bed. Anson was so struck by Fauquier's manliness in taking the loss of his fortune without complaint that he procured for Fauquier the governorship of Virginia.

This, then, was the man to whom Dr. Small introduced Tom Jefferson—a brilliant man, whose only vice was the gaming table. The talk at the Governor's mansion, however, was rarely of cards. It was of philosophy or economics or taxation, or the war which was coming to its close.

The war was to be known in Europe as the Seven Years' War, and in the American colonies as the French and Indian War. All Canada had now fallen to the British following the defeat of the French at the Battle of Abraham Heights. Furthermore the French had been cleared out of the Ohio Valley and in September 1760, the year that Tom Jefferson went to college, the French signed a treaty of surrender in Montreal which ended

French rule in any part of the North American continent.

The news of the French surrender was celebrated with joy throughout the colonies. For the people of the frontier it meant that there would be no more hostile Indian raids promoted by the French. For the people of the New England states, it meant that their produce, shipped to England, would not be at the mercy of French privateers. To Tom Jefferson it meant that the day was at hand when people would spill over the lovely folds of the Blue Ridge Mountains, pushing westward toward the Mississippi. The country was bound to grow and the direction in which it would grow was westward.

The country? What did he mean by "the country"? There wasn't a country really. There were thirteen colonies subject to Britain, which was the mother country.

And yet Tom Jefferson already felt about those thirteen colonies as if they constituted a country in their own right. They had the same king as Britain. But they each had their own legislative bodies. They also had their courts. Appeal from a decision of the colonial courts went to the higher English courts. And the legislatures of the colonial were called into session or dismissed by the colonial governor, who was the king's representative. That was perhaps right. But could the House of Parliament in England countermand a law passed by one of the colonial legislatures? And pursuing that question a little further, could the House of Parliament in England pass laws concerning the purely domestic affairs of the colonies?

There were many discussions about such subjects at Governor Fauquier's dinner table, Tom Jefferson listening while Dr. Small took one side, Fauquier another, and George Wythe mediated between the two.

George Wythe was reckoned the best Greek and Latin scholar in Virginia. He was a prominent lawyer in Williamsburg—a small, round-headed, quiet-spoken man; very soft-hearted and yet a stickler for the law. He surprised the whole of Williamsburg by freeing all his slaves and finding employment for them. Some he kept as servants in his big two-story brick house on Prince George Street, paying them in return for their work.

"An eccentric," the older planters said. "Too much study has gone to his head."

Soon anyone who wanted to find Tom Jefferson in the evening looked for him at the Governor's mansion, for he was there almost every night of the week. Once a week he played violin in a string quartet organized by Governor Fauquier. The quartet played the works of Corelli and Vivaldi and Handel. After a musical evening Fauquier would suggest a game of backgammon and send about the town for some gentlemen to play with. But Fauquier, with the loss of his fortune at cards many years before, had unwittingly taught Tom a lesson in gambling. Tom occasionally took a hand for politeness' sake, but never played deep, contenting himself with small stakes. He made a careful note of money lost in gambling to the last penny, and in later years would never allow a pack of cards to be seen in his home.

But it wasn't always easy for Tom Jefferson to remain in the company of Dr. Small, Fauquier, and George Wythe. Sometimes, during his studies, a fellow student would come in, turn over the table, and drag Tom out to witness some kind of sport in the town or join with his fellow students in a celebration at the Raleigh Tavern. Patrick Henry called on him often, the gay, laughing, brilliant man who always seemed more of an outdoorsman than a lawyer. He was a lawyer now, though. He had horrified the lawyers of Virginia by reading law for six weeks and then applying for admission to the bar. He hadn't bothered to wade through the huge dull volumes of Coke, the great English jurist, nor undertaken any of the other patient studies. But he passed his examination anyhow. He argued a case before his examiners with such ardent eloquence, with such forceful assertion of "nateral" rights, that they had no alternative but to admit him to practice.

Henry liked an active life. During the winter, when the courts were not in session, he rounded up all the overseers he could get together from the neighboring plantations and went off into the pine forests of the Fluvanna River, hunting deer. He lived in moccasins, deerskin breeches and hunting shirt, didn't bother to shave, hunted all day and joked and told stories around the campfires half the night. The overseers loved him. Tom Jefferson was awed by him. A lawyer in six weeks and one of the most sought-after in the colony! Here surely was genius.

Patrick Henry made good his vow to keep no books. He got payment in advance for his services, did what little reading on any particular case that was necessary, took it to court, and won it as often as not. He would handle four or five cases in one day without trouble, loved a jury trial, and could make the opposing counsel look like a fool with one deft phrase or even a gesture.

During these days in gay Williamsburg, Tom had many struggles with his conscience. Sometimes he wondered whether he wasn't a fool to spend so much time on study. He could become a great fox-hunter, or horseman and jockey. The whole colony would ring with his name if he rode the winning horse in a big race at Williamsburg. Or if he followed the example of Patrick Henry, concentrating on oratory rather than upon argument, he might become a brilliant lawyer without all the book study. Maybe he was wasting his time studying from dawn late into the night. But whenever he was tempted to give up his study and join in the round of pleasures of his fellow students he would ask himself what Dr. Small would do. And then he returned to his books. He learned to discipline himself so well that he could leave a ball at the height of the festivities to get back to his books.

And yet he remained popular. Patrick Henry never

failed to call on him when he came to town and shared his rooms with him. People found him serious but not stuffy. He could hold his own in a discussion with men twice and three times his years. Other students were called by nicknames or their first names. But gradually only his intimates called him Tom or Jeff. To others, even those who knew him quite well, he became Mr. Jefferson. They sensed that one day he would be a great man in the affairs of the colony, and that was their way of paying tribute to him.

After two years of study, Thomas Jefferson left William and Mary. He had largely wasted the first year in an unsuccessful battle with the attractions of the town. He had made up for it by studying twelve and fourteen hours a day in the second year.

Dr. Small returned to England, but before he went he secured for Tom a place in George Wythe's law office. There was then no formal course of law study in any college. A law student associated himself with a practicing lawyer, attended court, read all he could of law, and presented himself for examination when it was thought that he was ready.

Tom was nineteen years of age when he left William and Mary College in 1762. The long war between France and England had come to its close not only in the North American continent but in Europe and in India. The American colonies were safe from a French threat, and the nucleus of a British empire in India had come into being.

But the bill was high and had to be paid.

In London, Prime Minister George Grenville, surveying the costs of the war, decided that the American colonies must pay some part of the bill.

In Williamsburg, Thomas Jefferson began his study of law. And in Williamsburg too, Patrick Henry was retained in a case which concerned clergymen and tobacco.

Out of these strange and diverse elements there sprang in the short years ahead a storm that was to shake the whole world.

5

The official religion of the American colonies, established by the home government in England, was that of the Church of England. In different colonies there were varying degrees of tolerance for other religions, so that the Presbyterian Church had a good following in Virginia; and Roman Catholics, though a minority, might still worship in Pennsylvania. But the Church of England was the worship sanctioned by the home government and the salaries of the ministers of that church were paid from public funds.

In Virginia the recompense of a minister for his duties had been set at 16,000 pounds of tobacco a year, tobacco being in Virginia a better means of exchange than money.

The clergy liked that kind of payment. Tobacco always sold for a good price, so they were sure of an ample minimum salary. In some years when the crop was short, the price of tobacco went up and then they received, through the sale of their annual 16,000 pounds, even more money. They felt that was right—that the pastor should partake of the prosperity of his flock, and the price of tobacco, in all the history of Virginia, had never fallen so low as to leave parson or planter without a good living.

However, in 1758, "tobacco payment" was beginning to bring difficulties not only among the clergy but among merchants and planters. A man who had incurred a debt to the value of several hundred pounds of tobacco in one year, might find the price enormously increased—and his debt also—when he came to pay it off. If, for instance, he had incurred the debt when tobacco was valued at twopence a pound, and was called on to pay it off when the price of tobacco had gone up to fourpence a pound, his indebtedness had automatically doubled.

Creditors, of course, would demand payment of debts in years when tobacco was short, and many debtors were ruined by this practice. To regulate the situation, the Virginia General Assembly ruled in 1758 that, for purposes of paying debts and salaries, tobacco was to be valued at twopence per pound. A direct result of this was that ministers of the Church of England in Virginia were to receive in the future not 16,000 pounds of tobacco a year, but 32,000 pennies —the sum of one hundred and thirty-three pounds, six shillings and eightpence.

The clergymen were furious. Often they got far more than that through the sale of tobacco when the price was high. They scarcely ever got less. They pointed out angrily that the General Assembly, only ten years before, had specifically set their pay at sixteen hundred pounds of tobacco—not money—a year. And they emphasized that this previous act of the General Assembly, approved by the Governor of Virginia, had been further approved by the King himself in England. Did the General Assembly of Virginia think that it could now set itself above the King, substituting payment in money for payment in tobacco?

The issue cut even deeper than that. The clergymen were not even subject to the authority of the General Assembly in matters affecting their ministry. They were responsible to the Archbishop of Canterbury in England and the Archbishop himself was appointed by the King and answerable to the King. The General Assembly of Virginia then had no warrant or authority at all to interfere with the payment of the clergy. So the clergymen argued.

Nonetheless, Governor Fauquier approved the General Assembly's action in setting a money payment for the clergy of the Church of England in Virginia and the whole colony was split over the matter, which was argued with great heat in the mansions of the planters and in the public rooms of the taverns.

The general public was largely opposed to the clergy in the matter, for whatever a man's religion, he still payed taxes to support the Church of England. When the first year's salary was payable, and the clergymen got their salaries in money, some of them decided that they would appeal the matter directly to England. A suit was brought in the English courts and there the clergymen were upheld. The English courts ruled that they were entitled to payment in tobacco valued at the price of tobacco at the time of payment.

The English court decision did not sit well with the people of Virginia. The issue, they argued, was a domestic matter which concerned them alone. What did courts sitting in London know of the economics of the colony of Virginia? What right had English courts to interfere with laws passed by Virginia's parliament affecting only the people of Virginia? Was every little by-law passed by the General Assembly to be subject to the approval of an English court? If so, government became impossible, and the burgesses on Virginia were wasting their time trying to regulate matters in the colony. Whatever their decisions, an English court could set them aside.

The clergymen might have been warned by the temper of the people. But they were in a triumphant mood after the decision of the English court in their favor. Dr. James Maury, Tom Jefferson's old tutor, brought suit in Hanover County Court at Williamsburg for back payment of his salary from the year 1758. He had been paid at the price of twopence per pound for tobacco and tobacco had sold for more than that. He wanted the difference which he argued was due to him. It would be a substantial sum.

The Williamsburg court could not upset the ruling of the King's Privy Council in London—the court to which the clergymen had taken their case. All it could do was assess the damages owing to Dr. Maury and the other clergymen who joined him in the suit.

But the members of the House of Burgesses decided that although the case was lost, they would fight it anyway. If big damages were granted the clergymen, there would be a serious drain on the public treasury. The court award of damages had to be kept to an absolute minimum, and, looking around for someone to argue the case for them, they chose Patrick Henry.

He was a dark-horse choice. There were many more eminent lawyers in practice in Williamsburg who could argue long and well on the legal niceties of the matter. Henry knew little law and didn't pretend to know much. Six weeks of law study had been enough for him. The law, in his mind, could never set aside certain natural rights belonging to all men. He knew what those natural rights were and he was prepared to argue them before the highest court on earth in the face of all the monumental tomes written by the most eminent lawyers that ever lived.

When Henry was picked to defend the Burgesses, he was often in Tom Jefferson's rooms, and quite as often in the Apollo room of the Raleigh Tavern. He made practically no preparation of his case, which was so important that hundreds flocked into Williamsburg to attend the hearing. People buttonholed Patrick Henry in the streets and asked him what he thought of his chances. "We'll win, by thunder," Henry would say. And then he'd crack some joke or other and send them off chuckling and shaking their heads over this lawyer who looked like a backwoodsman wearing town clothes, and who was to represent the people of Virginia in what amounted to a contest with the Archbishop of Canterbury and, indeed, the King of England.

Tom Jefferson was concerned that Henry made so little preparation of his case. He hinted that there might be something in some of the old and neglected laws of England that would be of help to him. He offered to research the matter for him if that would be of any help. But Henry brushed aside Tom's concern.

"Men are not to be handicapped by laws passed a hundred, two hundred or a thousand years ago," he said. "The dead don't rule the living, crying out from their graves 'Thou shalt do this' and 'Thou shalt not do that.' Men live in their own times and rule themselves according to their times. Men make laws and change them when need be. But above all the laws they make, there are certain rights that no legislature can ever set aside and that belong to every man the day he is born."

"Such as?" asked Tom.

"The right to be free, for one," said Henry. "The right of every man to speak his mind. And to that I would add the right to say where his tax money is going, and how much he should pay in tax money anyway, and to whom."

"Well," said Tom dubiously, "I know about those rights. But the court must uphold the law. That is the function of a court . . ."

"You're wrong, Tom," said Henry. "The function of a court is to see that justice is done. Courts are courts of justice, and when I get before that jury I'll argue justice, and the devil with the law and all the precedents." And so Patrick Henry would not prepare his case in detail and Tom Jefferson was inclined to believe that Henry would lose the case. But he was determined to be present when the case was tried.

The courtroom was packed on the day of the trial, and only because he was reading law with the eminent George Wythe was Tom able to get a seat.

The clergy were there in large numbers, headed by Dr. James Maury. Tom couldn't even get through the press to exchange greetings with his old tutor.

The nature of the case demanded a jury to assess damages, and the jury, in their best clothes, sat to the side of the judicial bench, their wigs newly ironed and powdered, their clothes well pressed, the buckles gleaming on their shoes. In the front benches were the clergy, grave and dignified, clad in decent black and exchanging a few Latin phrases, to the awe of the less educated spectators. Council for the clergy was dressed with the decorum of a bishop, and oozed an air of piety and learning rivaling that of the petitioners.

Counsel for the defendants—Patrick Henry—was late. When the court was called to order, and the excited exchange of argument and opinion and greetings silenced under the stern cry of the court officer, Patrick Henry came pushing through the crowd, to take his place at the attorneys' table. He had a bundle of papers in his hands which he plomped carelessly on the table before him, contrasting with the beautifully prepared brief of his opponent, its various sections marked, for easy reference, with ribbons of red and green.

For a moment there was silence when Henry appeared. It was a silence of amazement, for the man was dressed in his ordinary street clothes. He had no fine London suit to his back, nor French lace at his throat and wrists. His suit, in fact, looked as his suits always looked, as if it were a size too small. His linen was clean but hurriedly pressed. He wore no wig, and his long dark hair was hastily gathered by a piece of ribbon at the nape of his neck. The ribbon in the opposing counsel's brief was of better quality than the strip of black cloth that Mr. Henry had snatched up in his lodgings to tie his hair with. Jury, clergy, and the general run of spectators gaped at him, those in the rear of the court standing on the benches to get a better view. Then there were a few snickers and a few remarks and soon the whole courtroom was commenting on his appearance and the miserable little bundle of papers he had brought in representing his brief. The bailiff had to call twice for silence before the audience settled down again. But even the judge, his fine French wig flowing gracefully over his shoulders, had been shaken out of his gravity by the appearance of Henry, and while the bailiff was calling for order was staring openly at the young attorney.

When the court was at last silent, and the clerk had read the title of the case before it, the judge pointed out that there was no question involved of whether or not the clergy were to receive compensation. That had already been ruled upon by the King's court in London. The duty of the present court was to assess the amount of compensation to be paid to Dr. James Maury and those associated with him. Counsel should then limit their arguments to this matter.

Counsel for the clergymen rose and, in a brief statement quoting tobacco prices backed up by many authorities, argued for a liberal payment running into several thousands of pounds. Counsel's analysis of tobacco prices since 1758 was authoritative; his argument convincing in regard to the loss to the clergymen by the withholding of money which might have been profitably invested. He presented his case forcefully, efficiently and briefly, and sat down to a murmur of commendation from his clients.

Patrick Henry had not expected so short a presentation. He had prepared a few principles in his mind that he intended to touch upon. But he hoped for time, while opposing counsel was talking, to get them into a proper order and elaborate them. Now, before he was ready, the judge turned to him, and asked him if he had any remarks to make in answer.

Henry rose to his feet. He wasn't prepared and he started badly. He stammered and repeated himself and at times was at a loss for words. There were a few murmurs of contempt from the audience. The opposing counsel looked smug and bored and the bank of clergymen smiled condescendingly at Henry. The effect was to anger Patrick Henry, and his anger quickly replaced his nervousness. Soon his voice was ringing through the courtroom and all were enthralled by every syllable he uttered. He had been warned by the judge to confine himself to the price of tobacco and the question of damages. He ignored the warning and addressed himself to the rights of men.

He began by tracing the history of the case, recalling that the House of Burgesses, a properly elected body with full authority, had ruled that the clergy were to be paid at twopence for a pound of tobacco. That ruling had affected others besides the clergy. Others had respected the ruling and abided by it. But the clergy had not respected it and had taken their case to the King's Privy Council in London. There the act of the House of Burgesses had been set aside—set aside by the privy council of the King; set aside, then, by the King himself.

Had the King the right to throw out the laws of the Virginia legislature? Was there this much power invested in one man that he could, with a little circle of advisers, declare which laws anywhere in the colonies were to stand and which laws were to fall? Was this a true monarch, entitled to the loyalty of his subjects? Or was this a tyrant who had forfeited all claims on loyalty by such an outrage against the people's elected representatives?

At this, counsel for the parsons leaped to his feet. "The gentleman has spoken treason!" he cried.

Henry, flushed but undaunted, plunged on, hammering away at the authority of the King, both personal and as expressed through his privy council.

He turned then on the clergymen themselves. They were members of a calling whose duty it was to teach the Gospel. One of the prime functions of an established church was to encourage the cheerful support of those laws which the people had passed for their own prosperity and good government. But the defendant had failed in this essential Christian function. Instead, motivated by private greed the clergy had thrown aside the ruling others had accepted and thus had given an example of rebellion against the just laws of the House of Burgesses as sanctioned by the governor of Virginia. More than that. The clergy were supposed in their calling to comfort the sick, give aid and money and food to the poor and uplift the downtrodden. But instead they were stealing the pauper's last coin, and demanding the milch cow of the widow. They were "rapacious harpies" who would take the last blanket off a sick woman's bed to satisfy their salaries. So he went on, whipping the clergymen with his scorn, flinging the price of tobacco in their faces until, blushing and ashamed, they left the court one by one in confusion. When Patrick Henry had done, there was complete silence in the courtroom. A whole new concept of thinking had been opened for the audience and they were awed and exhilarated by what they had heard. The authority of established church and hereditary king had been exposed as a tyranny to which they had submitted without thinking. Now their eyes were opened for them.

The judge cleared his throat and addressed himself to the jury. "The question before the court," he replied, "is one of damages. The jury has heard the arguments and will now retire and assess what damages are due."

The jury was out for only five minutes.

"You have deliberated the matter of damages?" asked the judge.

"Yes, your Honor," said the foreman.

"And what damages have you agreed upon as proper?"

"One penny," was the reply.

Suddenly all was in an uproar. People jumped cheering to their feet. They rushed past the wooden barrier separating the court proper from the audience room, grabbed Henry, hoisted him on their shoulders and carried him cheering into the streets, around the town and then to Tom Jefferson's chambers. The celebration of the victory lasted all night. The news spread like a brush fire through all the colonies. The name of Patrick Henry, well-enough known in Virginia, was now known in every one of the colonies. It was a name people associated with liberty—a new kind of liberty based upon natural rights.

When the hubbub died down, Tom Jefferson began to think the case over. There was no doubt in his mind that Henry's talent for oratory rather than his knowledge of law had won the day. But there was a danger in this. If oratory were misapplied, then good laws, arrived at after a great deal of reasoning and investigation, could be set aside under the emotional sway of an orator.

Tom decided to look into the legal aspects of an established church—to see whether there was any body of law making it proper for a government to set up an official religion and tax people, irrespective of their private beliefs, to support that religion.

His studies took him back through English law to Anglo-Saxon law, from which English law derived. To read the old Anglo-Saxon laws as they were laid down he had to study Anglo-Saxon. He mastered the language but could find nowhere in the early laws any legal relationship between the Saxon kings and the Christian religion.

He discovered that, in the course of centuries, King and Church had found it to their advantage mutually to support each other. But there was no warrant at all for a king or any government to control the conscience of the people. The situation had been foisted upon the public gradually and without their knowledge. In short, what Henry had known instinctively to be a natural right—freedom of worship—Thomas Jefferson found to be so not only by instinct but by patient search through scores of lawbooks.

He suspected that there might be many other natural rights of the people which in course of time had been eroded away. These rights had been taken from the people because the people were not conscious of their existence. Some of them were laid out in the great document, Magna Carta, signed by King John of England at the insistence of his barons. But there were many many others which had been forfeited or were perhaps in danger of being lost through the ignorance of the general public.

He spoke with Patrick Henry about these rights, and the two debated whether some kind of new Magna Carta was not needed which would establish principles that no court had the right to violate.

Tom had read the works of Locke, the English philosopher, dealing with the theory of government, and ardently believed that governments should be established by the consent of the people as Locke propounded, and the form of government should be changed when needed to coincide with the will of the people. He had had many talks on this subject with Patrick Henry. Though Henry loved dancing and hunting and company, he could be serious too, and was never so serious as when he suspected that some wrong was being foisted on the people of his beloved Virginia.

Meanwhile, Tom Jefferson continued with his studies. He worked out a heroic schedule for himself. He got out of bed as soon as it was dawn, and was up until midnight studying his books. His studies took him into every area of science and thought—agriculture, chemistry, anatomy, astronomy, philosophy, ethics, history, and religion. He bought books by the dozen, not merely to read but to study. He started keeping a record of his own about his work in a journal which he called his Commonplace Book. In this he noted anything that particularly struck him during his studies—quotations from Shakespeare and summaries of legal decisions, entered side by side with observations on the movement of the planets and the temperature at midday on a particular date.

He even found time to play his violin, and for twelve years reckoned that he practiced three hours a day. If there was a good play at the playhouse, Tom Jefferson found time to see it. If a case of any interest was being argued in court, Tom Jefferson was there listening to the arguments advanced and later looking up the legal precedents.

One of his friends, John Page, marveled at the discipline young Jefferson displayed in all things. He would tear himself away from any pleasure if his watch told him that it was time to get to work. Even in the middle of an animated discussion, Tom Jefferson would look at his watch and excuse himself, saying he had to work but begging that the discussion be continued later.

Work, tedious to others, was his delight. As athletes train to climb mountains, so Tom Jefferson trained. But the mountains he was to climb were those of the mind, from whose peaks he would get a breath-taking view of the future of free men.

6

The Seven Years' War, and that branch of it fought in America which came to be known as the French and Indian Wars, ended in 1763. Britain had won a great victory over France, an ancient foe, but at an enormous cost. She had had to maintain armies in Europe, in India, and in America. She had had to keep big fleets at sea ranging the world from the Spanish coast to the shores of India and of Massachusetts. Her people had been taxed and double and triple taxed with the greatest ingenuity to support such a vast endeavor. Now came the need for even more revenue so that Britain could safeguard what she had won during the war—her new possessions in India, and her thirteen colonies in America now for the first time free of any threat of a French envelopment.

The thirteen American colonies, in Britain's view, had not behaved very well during the French and Indian Wars. They were separate colonies with separate charters (in cases where they had charters) and with separate governors appointed by the King, and with separate legislative bodies.

They ran themselves to the extent they were allowed, as separate little countries jealous of any special privilege a neighboring colony might be granted. Those that had a frontier with the old French territories, like Virginia and Pennsylvania, sent men and supplies actively to the support of Britain's army during the French and Indian Wars.

A young surveyor and planter, George Washington of Virginia, served with distinction during the war. On his return to Virginia where he was captain of the Virginia militia, he was given a reception that eclipsed anything in living memory. Taking his seat as a new delegate to the House of Burgesses in 1759, he received the thanks of the House for his services to the colony. He rose to reply but could make none. He blushed and stammered and trembled, but not a word came from him.

"Sit down, Mr. Washington," said the speaker.

"Your modesty equals your valor, and that surpasses the power of any language I possess."

But other colonies, those on the coast or those having no border on the western frontier, took as little part in the French and Indian Wars as they could. Rather, they used the war to increase the powers of their legislatures. When the royal governor asked for supplies or for men the legislatures refused them, or decided to appoint committees to consider them, or delayed in one way or another until some privilege they wished was granted them. Often they asked for privileges the governors had no power to grant. The governors, hard pressed by the commanders in the field for men and supplies, were sometimes forced to grant these privileges anyway, hoping to justify themselves later by pointing to the urgency of war.

As for the merchants—the shipping men importing and exporting goods, many of those in the New England states saw in the war with France an opportunity for profit. Their big trade was in molasses obtained from the French West Indies. The war cut that trade off and the price of molasses went temptingly high.

The governor would then be petitioned to allow a ship to go past the British blockade of the French islands under a flag of truce to release American hostages, who, it was claimed, were suffering terrible torments in French jails. Pleading letters from them were produced, begging for relief and saying that the alternative was a lingering death.

Under such pressure the governors would at times allow a ship to sail to bring back these prisoners. Public subscriptions quickly raised the ransom money demanded by the French. The ship sailed and returned—carrying hostages to be sure, but laden down also with molasses which was smuggled ashore at night and later disposed of at great profit.

The war indeed had the effect common to wars—it turned traders into smugglers. Massachusetts merchants of high renown traded illegally with the same French enemy against whom, in the dark forests of the Ohio Valley, Washington was leading the militia of Virginia.

There was little unity then among the thirteen American colonies in the war against France. Each looked to its own welfare, and many were mostly concerned with seeing that they gave no more to the war in men and materials than their neighbors. Some flatly declared that none of their men or materials were to be used outside of the territory of the colony. Maryland would fight the French if the French ever got to Maryland. But not before. So it went.

But though the war did not unify the colonies, the peace that followed did, for it confronted them all with the same threat—the threat of taxation to pay Britain's war debts.

Studying his lawbooks in Williamsburg, talking world affairs over with George Wythe and Patrick Henry, with Dabney Carr and John Page, Tom Jefferson became interested in the question of taxation and the theories that lay behind taxes.

The first postwar tax levied by Prime Minister Grenville in England on the American colonies was a tax on molasses. It hardly affected Virginia, whose principal item of trade was tobacco. It fell heavily, however, on the merchants of New England who had been in the habit of importing molasses from the French and Dutch as well as the British West Indies. The molasses was turned in New England into rum and found a profitable market. To pay for the molasses, the New England merchants exported lumber, horses, hides, and other produce to the West Indian islands.

The new tax imposed a duty of threepence a gallon on molasses imported from any of the non-British West Indian islands. The effect on the New Englanders was disastrous. They couldn't pay such a tax. They had to get their molasses in the future from the British islands only. The planters in the British islands obtained a monopoly in the export of molasses to the American colonies. They raised the price. Soon the wharfs of New York and Boston were overstocked with unsalable lumber warping in the weather.

Such a flood of lumber had already gone to the British West Indian planters that they needed no more. The same held for horses and other exports. And the New Englanders couldn't pay for the molasses in money. Money was very short in the colonies.

There wasn't enough available in New England to make the purchase of molasses a cash trade.

Still, the Molasses Act or Sugar Act, as it was called, did not hurt Virginia and most Virginians were of the opinion that it wasn't their business. But Tom Jefferson and Patrick Henry and the younger men of Williamsburg took a different view. They studied copies of the act and found that in the preamble mention was made of the need for "new provisions and regulations . . . for improving the revenue of this Kingdom [Britain] . . . it is just and necessary that a revenue should be raised [the act read] . . . for defraying the expenses of defending, protecting, and securing the same."

"Very curious," said Patrick Henry. "I wonder what's the meaning behind that."

"It could mean that the British Parliament considers it has the right to tax us here in the colonies to raise revenue to meet Britain's expenses," said Jefferson.

"Oh, come now!" said Dabney Carr. "They've never done that before. They've imposed duties regulating trade. That's all this is. It's a duty on importing French and Dutch molasses. And I think it's a good one. I hear those New England merchants made fortunes during the war, trading in molasses with the enemy while we in Virginia were fighting the French."

"Dabney," said Tom with a smile, "it never does to be deceived by the obvious. Obviously this is a tax on foreign molasses. But what isn't so obvious is that the opening phrases of this act assert the right of Britain to 'establish new provisions and regulations' to raise money. And note that this is an act—it isn't a proposal. It has already received the approval of Parliament. I tell you that, with such an act in my hands, I could defend Britain's right to tax her American colonies before any court in the world."

"You read too much into it, Tom," said Dabney Carr. "You've spent so long with your nose in books that you're losing your balance."

Tom Jefferson shook his head. "Liberties are lost because people are too lazy to read the law closely," he said. "There isn't a doubt in my mind that this act establishes the right of Britain to tax us in America, if need be, to pay Britain's debts."

"Well, we're British, aren't we?" said John Page. "The King's our king. What's wrong with being taxed?"

"There's this wrong with it," said Patrick Henry; "we have no say in England's Parliament. By thunder, they could take every penny we make—suck us dry and pay no taxes themselves. And we wouldn't be able to do a thing about it."

"You're talking about Englishmen," retorted Page. "Not Frenchmen or Prussians. They're a free people. They are not tyrants. They respect liberty."

"They're a free people," said Patrick Henry dryly, "because they fought for every freedom they got—fought their own government."

"Meaning?" asked Page.

"Meaning nobody gives you freedom. You have to

fight to obtain it and fight to protect it. That's the plain history of the whole world, Mr. Page."

"By thunder," said Page, "you're a man who is readily moved perilously close to treason."

"You know what treason is?" demanded Patrick Henry hotly. "It's an unsuccessful attempt to overthrow a government—and a fig for treason, I say."

Jefferson shook his head. "I don't agree with that," he said. "I'd say that treason was an attempt to deprive any man of that freedom which is his gift from birth. Governments can be guilty of treason as well as the people who are governed."

There were others in Virginia who were equally concerned over the Sugar Act. Prominent among them was George Washington. He was thirty-two years of age at the time, a tall athletic rawboned man, very mild in his behavior and somewhat sober in his dress for a Virginian. He didn't affect the Dutch and French clothes and laces of the other Virginia planters, and had no liveried Negro outriders on the horses that brought his coach to Williamsburg. Indeed, he didn't often use his coach, but preferred to ride to Williamsburg on a horse whenever he had to visit the capital as a recently elected member of the House of Burgesses.

He had a great reputation as a military leader and he was now making another reputation as a man of common sense. He stood halfway between the conservative and wealthy planters of the Tidewater, who would bend over backward rather than give direct offense to England, and the fiery representatives of the Piedmont, like Patrick Henry, who detested English interference in the colonies' affairs.

Washington had many friends and business acquaintances in London, who kept him well supplied with the latest news. He had heard that the King intended to maintain a standing army of 10,000 soldiers in the American colonies, and that £300,000 a year was to be raised from the colonies to pay for their keep and also help reduce Britain's war debt.

He spoke of these things to the other delegates of the House of Burgesses. He spoke gravely and quietly, which in itself made a big impression upon his fellow legislators.

"In sum," one of them asked, "what do you think is likely to happen?"

"In sum," replied Washington, "I think this Sugar Act is but the start. There are likely to be other measures that will fall as heavily on Virginia as this present act falls upon New York and Massachusetts."

"What do you know of this man Grenville—what kind of temper has he?"

"I hear he is stiff and dour and set in his opinions," replied Washington. "You will remember that it was said of Dashwood, Chancellor of the Exchequer under the old government, that his knowledge of accounts was confined to reckoning tavern bills and that a sum of five figures was, to him, an impenetrable mystery? Well, Grenville is the opposite. He is a financier who could himself count every penny that comes into the British treasury and reckon the compound interest on it without resort to pen and paper. That's what I hear from London."

"A hard man to do business with, then."

Washington nodded. "So it seems," he said. "But we must do business with him. The people of Britain are so heavily taxed they will not pay another penny. No measure for raising additional taxes in Britain has any chance of passing the Houses of Parliament. There would be rioting. The sentiment is that we in the colonies have gone by tax free so far. Unless I am mistaken, we are all about to be presented with a big bill on which payment will be enforced."

The big bill was not long coming. It came in the form of the Stamp Act—a measure which Grenville regarded as extremely mild and one to which the colonies could not possibly take any exception. However, to be absolutely sure that no one in America could claim that the act was suddenly imposed on the people without anyone having a chance to debate it, Prime Minister Grenville announced that the act would not be enforced until several months after its passage through the House of Commons. The colonial legislatures would then have plenty of time to debate it and pass their views on to London. Also, people would have time to get used to it. The act was passed in January, 1765, and was to come into effect in November of the same year.

Thomas Jefferson, though still putting in at times fifteen hours' study a day at his lawbooks, was often at the mansion of Governor Fauquier as a dinner guest. Fauquier liked Jefferson. He liked him for his learning, his hard work, the depth of his mind, his excellent manners, and his ability to conduct himself with grace in the highest society. He often spoke to him about his reading, and recommended to him the writings of Bolingbroke, one of the greatest authors on the theory of government at that time. He was not angry when, after dinner, Tom would excuse himself from the table saying he had to go back to his studies.

"You do well to work hard now, Mr. Jefferson," Fauquier would say. "A month's hard work now will save you a year's frustration later in life. Depend upon it."

But sometimes Tom would stay after dinner, particularly if George Wythe or Peyton Randolph, speaker of the Virginia Assembly and a kinsman of Tom's on his mother's side, was among the guests. Then the talk would be about the impending Stamp Act, for Fauquier wanted to sound out his guests and report to the home government on feeling toward the act.

These discussions never became angry. They were an exchange among gentlemen on a public matter. But it was plain to Tom that there was a deep difference of opinion between the Virginians on the one hand, and Fauquier, representing the British crown, on the other.

Fauquier put the British point of view and put it well. "We've been paying a stamp tax in England for years," he said. "It is the lightest of our imposts, I assure you, gentlemen. And it works for the public good.

No document is legal unless it has a stamp upon it—a certificate of marriage, a will, a transfer of goods from one party to another, clearance papers for a ship leaving harbor—all these documents in England have a stamp on them. They are illegal without them. There is a benefit, then, in making their documents legal and that benefit I am sure will appeal to you, gentlemen, who are so learned in the law. How many times has a document presented in court—a will, say, or a deed of land—been contested as improperly drawn? There are a hundred such cases a month. But with a stamp on them, the documents are legal, must be so accepted in court, and there is no argument about them. In all conscience I must say I regard the act as beneficial in every way."

"It is the wrong time to impose such an act, sir," said Peyton Randolph. "Things are in a bad way in the colonies. The end of the recent war has brought the usual depression. Unemployment is high in the northern colonies and we begin to feel the pinch here in Virginia. Boston is full of unemployed and New York also. I hear that in Rhode Island, land values as a result of unemployment have tumbled to half their previous price. The Sugar Act fell heavily on the people. To follow up now with this Stamp Act will beggar them."

"Oh come, sir," said Fauquier. "These postwar depressions are only temporary. Before the act is in effect all will be prosperous again, no doubt. I note," he added with a smile, "that you still ride in your coach and six, and Mrs. Randolph's new Paris gown is, I assure you, as elegant as anything that graces the ballrooms of London. What do you think of this matter, Mr. Jefferson?"

"I think it wrong in principle," said Tom. "It is a matter of our being taxed without our having a say in the matter. It opens the door wide to increasing taxation on the same basis—taxation without representation."

"You're mistaken there, I fancy, Mr. Jefferson," said Fauquier. "Certainly you have a say in the matter. There is a whole year in which to debate the tax and in which to present your opinions through your own assemblies in proper form. The Virginia Assembly, as are the various legislatures of all the other colonies, is assured of an ear in London. Your own Dr. Franklin is there on your behalf as Colonial Agent, and is close to the Prime Minister—far closer indeed than I am," he added ruefully.

"That is true," said Tom. "But no petition passed by the Virginia Assembly will ever be read on the floor of the House of Commons if it concerns this tax. There is a rule of the House of Commons, if I am correctly informed, that no petition from the colonies affecting financial matters may be introduced on the floor of the House."

"The reason for the rule," said Fauquier, "is that the whole business of the House would otherwise be hopelessly delayed by hosts of petitions from all the colonies every time a customs officer collected a little duty from an American merchant. It is a very reasonable rule. There are other avenues of protest open to the colonies."

"But there is no representation, sir," said Tom firmly. "An Englishman in England, if taxed, has a representative in the Parliament that taxes him through whom he can directly protest. No American has any such representative. We are voiceless in Parliament, and if heard at all, are heard only through a third party who is not a citizen of the country."

"Well, you're heard with remarkable effect," said Fauquier. "Colonel Isaac Barré made an impassioned defense of you in the House of Commons, denouncing the tax and calling you all Sons of Liberty. In Boston and New York some of the rougher elements are organizing themselves into bands and calling themselves Sons of Liberty, after Barré, and causing all kinds of trouble. I'm sure we won't have that kind of nonsense here in Virginia." He glanced at Peyton Randolph, the most influential man in the Assembly.

"Quite right," said Randolph. "We haven't the same rabble to deal with here. A few hotheads among the younger delegates—but not riotous."

"Mr. Jefferson is acquainted with a few of the 'hotheads,'" said Fauquier with a smile. "That is, if I may for the moment describe Mr. Patrick Henry as a hothead. Though I will admit privately that I rejoiced in his victory in the parsons' case. It was a victory for me. What do you say, Mr. Jefferson? Do you know his views on this Stamp Act?"

"I know he is opposed to it, sir," said Tom. "And I must add in all honesty, so am I."

"Well," said Fauquier, "it is the mark of youth to be rebellious. I note that the younger people oppose the act on principles of representation. The older sort are not so concerned with principles as with the imposing of a new tax during a time of depression."

"Allow me to correct you," said George Wythe gently. "We older sort are also opposed to the act on principle. We believe that as Englishmen at home would not submit to taxation without representation, neither should we. But we are not hotheads. We do not believe the mother country a tyrant, nor the British Parliament a body set upon enslaving the people of the colonies. We believe that by representation, decently made through our assemblies, the matter will be resolved. We trust that that will be so."

"That has always been the case in the past, gentlemen," said Fauquier smoothly. "And I think the mother country, after the expenses of the recent war, and with her people at home outrageously taxed, may expect, without injustice, to raise additional revenue here in the colonies, particularly since one outcome of the war was to make us here safe from the French. I give you my word, gentlemen, that the money to be raised by the Stamp Tax is to be spent here, and not, as some say, on reducing Britain's national debt. It will be spent on maintaining troops in the country—some ten thousand, I believe—for the purpose of protecting the colonies from the French and from the Indian tribes."

He smiled at his guests. "The ladies, I am sure, will have no objection to the troops," he said. "Nothing seems to make a man so handsome or dashing as to be wearing the uniform of one of his Majesty's regiments. The King's officers were in great demand at balls and levees, as you recall during the recent war. The money raised here will be spent here and will in itself serve to stimulate trade. Upon my word, the more I think of the measure, the more enchanting it appears—providing escorts for the ladies, protection for the colonies, a stimulus to trade, avoiding litigation over documents, and when applied to marriage licenses, making all weddings thoroughly legal . . . something I know you gentlemen will agree is in the best interests of society. The young man in love, lavishing gifts on his bride, will hardly hold back from paying twenty shillings stamp tax on a wedding license to make her fully his own."

When the party broke up, Tom walked home to his lodgings with George Wythe. "The Governor puts forward a persuasive case for the Stamp Tax," said Wythe, eying Tom closely.

"That is the Governor's job," said Tom. "But the Governor avoids the principle. And the principle is one of no taxation without representation."

"I think there is likely to be trouble," said Wythe slowly. "I am not a man to compromise on a principle.

But the part of wisdom is to maintain the principle with as little trouble as possible."

They passed the Raleigh Tavern. Looking through the leaded windows of the Apollo room they saw a crowd of younger men gathered around Patrick Henry, who, pulling at intervals on a pipe of tobacco, was talking heatedly to them. Though they could not hear what he was saying there was no doubt that he was discussing the Stamp Act, for it was the topic of all such gatherings. George Wythe looked from the tavern down the street to where the House of Burgesses loomed in the moonlight.

"In a civilized society," he said slowly, "there are two sources of government—the tavern and the legislative assembly. And often the tavern is the superior body and rules the other."

7

The delay in the enforcing of the Stamp Act, which Prime Minister Grenville had hoped would result in the colonies' getting used to the idea and accepting it, had a contrary effect.

Rather than bow to the tax, the more the people of the thirteen colonies thought about it, the more they resented it. There were riots in New York and Philadelphia instigated often by printers who, as publishers of newspapers, saw their circulation threatened by the tax which would have to be paid on every paper purchased in the colonies.

There were riots by tavernkeepers who would now have to pay a tax for serving liquor. Some of these riots were brought about by self-interest. But beyond this was a sense of outrage that the people were to be taxed by a parliament to which they could not elect a single representative. The resentment seemed stronger and more bitter among the small farmers and traders, artisans and storekeepers.

Tom Jefferson noted that in Virginia the higher placed a man was in society, the less forthright was his objection to the Stamp Act. Some indeed took the view suggested by Governor Fauquier that the act was a most benevolent measure, and applied for positions as Stamp Tax collectors. The post would bring them as much as £300 a year—a nice sum. It also brought opportunity to put others in the way of making a little money as district collectors, thus enabling a Stamp Tax collector to build up a little empire of people who were indebted to him.

Jefferson, though he belonged to the higher class of Virginia society, sympathized with the tradesmen and storekeepers and little farmers. All but voiceless in their own legislative assembly, where the rich planters were overwhelmingly represented, they had no influence in England at all. Yet they were the people on whom the tax would fall most heavily—paid in every receipt they issued for goods bought or sold, in every newspaper they bought, in every tankard of beer or tot of rum they drank at the end of the day.

The gentle George Wythe, Tom reflected, was right to say that the tavern was the superior legislative body. The tavern was the parliament of these unrepresented people. It was here that they discussed their grievances; here that they learned that their fellows in other colonies felt much the same way about the Stamp Tax as they did. And it was here, without formal debate or the passage of any resolution, that they decided they would not continue voiceless and unrepresented in their government.

A big change came over the colonies in the period of grace before the enforcement of the Stamp Act. It was a change that Tom Jefferson noted and that Patrick Henry helped to bring about. In essence it was a change from separation to unity. People started to think of the colonies as a whole. Massachusetts was no longer foreign to Virginia or Pennsylvania foreign to South Carolina. Two words began to occur more and more frequently in discussion—"America" and "liberty."

Soon the words were combined and became "American liberty." At first the phrase meant the same liberty for Americans as was extended to Englishmen. After a little while, the phrase began to mean more than that—a liberty greater for Americans than that which was afforded Englishmen of the day; in short, a liberty based on "natural rights" with which neither King nor Parliament nor House of Burgesses nor any legislative body anywhere could tamper.

The small farmers and people from the Piedmont elected Patrick Henry to the House of Burgesses in 1765, the year of the Stamp Act.

He soon proved his worth.

The Treasurer of the colony, a former speaker of the House of Burgesses, was John Robinson, a wealthy, generous, kindly planter of the Tidewater. As Treasurer he had control of public funds. Quite often he lent money to his planter friends temporarily in need. First he lent his own money, but when he was short himself, he took to lending the public money, quite sure that his friends, being gentlemen, and he being a gentleman, the debts would be repaid, the public treasury reimbursed, and that there was nothing dishonest in the action.

But the debts were not repaid. The Tidewater planters, living lavishly, paying huge prices for blood horses and coaches built in London, for dresses for their wives made of the best European materials, and spending heavily on entertainments that lasted a week or more, did not take in as much as they paid out. Far from being able to repay their original debts, they applied to the obliging John Robinson for more funds. He supplied them—from the public treasury.

The time arrived however when John Robinson discovered that the whole of his own private fortune was not sufficient to cover the funds he had borrowed from the public coffers to accommodate his friends. And his friends, gentlemen every one of them to the last inch, were not businessmen. They couldn't pay back the debts.

Ruin and disgrace then confronted Robinson. And so he consulted among the members of the Assembly, many of whom had received loans from him. They came up with a plan which would save the situation. They proposed a bill under which money might be advanced to individuals in need from public funds—making the public treasury a loan agency.

It was argued in support of the bill that the advancing of funds to individuals from the public coffers would help them to develop or buy property which would increase the wealth of the colony of Virginia. That might have been true. But the bill would also save John Robinson from ruin. If the bill passed, he would thus officially transfer to the treasury the loans he had unwisely made to his friends, making them legal.

When Henry read the bill, he became suspicious. He knew nothing of John Robinson's loans, but he wondered how many poor farmers in the Piedmont would ever get a loan from the public treasury to buy a plow or a couple of oxen. He suspected that none would. The loans would go to the men with big estates who would spend the money, not on pioneering but on parties.

He then rose in the House of Burgesses to oppose

the bill. He was a new member, roughly dressed as always, with an outdoorsman's awkwardness which seemed exaggerated in the dignified quiet of the chamber. Tom Jefferson stood outside the door to listen to what Henry had to say. Tom was not a member of the chamber and so had to stand in the hallway, straining to hear what was said.

Henry did not falter in his address. He launched vigorously into an attack against lending public money to private individuals. What was the matter with borrowing money through the usual channels—from friends or from bankers or other sources? he asked. Any man of character and of honesty could obtain funds in this way. Those who could not were lacking in character or determination or the desire to work.

"What, sir!" he cried, addressing the speaker. "Is it proposed to reclaim the spendthrift from his dissipation and extravagance by filling his pockets with money?" And then he turned and surveyed the rich and idle planters of the Tidewater, who reddened at his words. The whole proposition, Henry went on, was based on favoritism—favoritism which would support the wealthy in their idleness at the expense of the poor who paid the taxes.

His one speech killed the bill. All the representatives from the poorer sections, from the Piedmont, voted against it. Those voting for it were from the wealthy Tidewater. But there were not enough of them present. The bill failed to pass, and Virginia had witnessed the open split, long in developing, between the pioneers of the Piedmont and the aristocracy of the Tidewater.

But Henry had attacked the bill on principle, not out of enmity for Robinson. Robinson's mishandling of public funds only came to light four years later at his death. Until then, his fellow planters, forming a conspiracy of self-interest, kept the matter hidden.

Not long after that came Henry's attack in the House of Burgesses on the Stamp Act. He had spoken against it often enough in the Apollo room of the Raleigh Tavern and with his friends. But during the actual debate in the House of Burgesses he was either absent or said little.

Tom Jefferson was puzzled by Henry's action. Why was he so fiery in private but so meek in the House of Burgesses? Was he afraid perhaps that a charge of treason might be brought against him? Was he, as the richer men said, merely a braggart, full of sound and threats but lacking in courage when a major issue was to be faced? For this Stamp Act wasn't an issue concerning the payment of parsons, or the loaning of money from the Virginia treasury. It concerned the King and Parliament of England. Whoever attacked the act attacked the King, the King's ministers and the King's Parliament.

All through the debate then, Henry remained quietly in the background, while the Burgesses expressed their regrets over the act, and patiently framed a petition to the King to put the act aside and framed also a memorial to the House of Commons, objecting to the act with the greatest reasonableness and courtesy.

Peyton Randolph, Tom's kinsman, took a prominent part in these debates, steering the language so that the protest was made but no offense was given in making it. Then, when all was done to the satisfaction of the Assembly and the wording of the petition to the King and the memorial to the House of Commons approved to the last comma, a vote was taken to send them both off. The business had been attended to. Members began packing to return to their mansions up the river. Many of them left. Still Henry held his peace.

When most of the Tidewater representatives had gone home, although the Assembly was still in session, Henry at last rose and asked leave to address the House on the subject of the Stamp Act and to present some motions affecting it for the consideration of members. The Speaker was astounded. The matter had been dealt with. Why reopen it now? But he had no right to refuse to hear Henry.

Again Tom Jefferson stood in the doorway of the chamber, not being allowed to enter since he was not a delegate. The speech he heard from Henry, rushing from him like a roaring torrent, surpassed in fire and eloquence anything he had ever previously heard from his friend.

Henry cut the same unimpressive figure. There were titters at his homely clothes, his unpowdered hair, his curious awkwardness which made him, when standing, to seem all elbows and knees. The speaker had a little difficulty securing a hearing for him. But as soon as he started talking, there were no more titters. A stillness like death descended on the House, broken only by the voice of Patrick Henry, now so low his listeners could scarcely catch what he was saying, now so strong and loud his words seemed to fill not only the chamber but the whole world.

Henry went straight to the point—denouncing the pretensions of the British Parliament to levy taxes on the people of the American colonies. Americans, he said, had the same rights as Englishmen. No Englishman would submit to being taxed without representation. No American should do so either. The rights of Englishmen and Americans were bound together in the matter and were equally threatened.

To tax Americans without representation would open the door to the taxation of Englishmen without representation, and so ancient liberties, most desperately won, were now endangered. What confronted the people of Virginia was the growing presence of tyranny which had been resisted time and again in the great days of Greece and Rome and of the mother country, England.

"Caesar," cried Henry, "had his Brutus, Charles the First his Cromwell, and George the Third—"

Suddenly he was interrupted by cries of "Treason . . . treason . . ." from all parts of the chamber. He waited until the hubbub had died down.

"And George the Third," he continued, "may profit

by their example. Sir [addressing the Speaker] if *this* be treason, make the most of it."

Then he took a sheaf of papers untidily folded from his pocket and said he wished to move seven resolves bearing on the rights of the people of Virginia, for the approval of the House.

The first five of these resolves were to the effect that Americans possessed all the rights of Englishmen; that the principle of no taxation without representation was an essential part of the British constitution, which applied fully to all Americans; that, as a result, it was plain that Virginia alone enjoyed the right to tax Virginians, since Virginians had representation only in their own House of Burgesses.

The sixth and seventh resolves shook the members into a profound silence—partly in horror at the daring, partly in fright at their significance. One declared that Virginians were "not bound to yield obedience to any law or ordinance whatever designed to impose any taxation whatsoever upon them, other than the laws or ordinances of the General Assembly."

The other stated that "any person who shall, by speaking or writing, assert or maintain that any person or persons other than the General Assembly of the Colony, have any right or power to impose or lay any taxation on the people here, shall be deemed an enemy of his Majesty's Colony."

After the first paralyzed silence which greeted the reading of these resolutions, an uproar broke out in the chambers. The Piedmont and up-country members of the Assembly were cheering Henry loudly. The Tidewater aristocrats were shouting him down, denouncing him as a hothead whose excesses would bring heavy penalties from England. The Speaker had great difficulty in restoring order so that individual members could express their views on the resolves.

Against Henry were many of Tom Jefferson's friends —the moderate and reasonable George Wythe with whom Tom was still studying law; Peyton Randolph, another kinsman of Thomas' and at that time Attorney General of Virginia. And also against him was Colonel Richard Bland, an eminent student of constitutional law, whose face had something of the color and texture of the old parchments over which he pored incessantly.

The opposition insisted that the petition and memorial already sent to Parliament and the King covered all that Henry proposed and in language which would not give offense. No reply had been received to these communications. To come roaring in now with these inflammatory resolves would ensure that whatever reply *was* received, was contrary to the colony's interests.

But Henry won the victory. Although his sixth and seventh resolutions failed to pass, the first five, asserting the right of Virginians to tax themselves, were passed, some by very narrow margins. Indeed, the fifth resolution, passed by only 20 to 19, was subsequently ruled out.

Nonetheless Patrick Henry, a member of the House

of Burgesses for less than a month, had secured a clear victory over men who had been delegates for a dozen years and more. He had outmaneuvered them by waiting until there were only 39 members out of a total of 116 present in the House. With a tiny minority from the Piedmont he had won a victory over the huge majority from the Tidewater—and won it on a crucial issue, challenging the authority of the King and his Parliament over the people of Virginia.

"By thunder," cried Peyton Randolph to Tom Jefferson as he stormed angrily from the chamber, "I would have given five hundred pounds for one more vote. Five hundred pounds. But the damage is done now and the giddy hotheads have carried the day."

8

The Stamp Act was followed by the Stamp Act riots—riots which erupted in every one of the thirteen colonies with a violence that astounded the royal governors and their intimate circle of advisers.

Patrick Henry became, overnight, not merely a Virginia hero but a national hero—for there was beginning to be an American nation now, as the colonies united under the banner of "No Taxation without Representation." His Seven Resolves, known as the Virginia Resolves, were printed in every newspaper of importance in the colony. Among the conservatives they produced a sense of outrage and some called them treason. But the overwhelming majority of Americans hailed them as sacred—resolves for which they were prepared to fight and indeed to die.

Henry became the hero of the Sons of Liberty—bands of young people (and some of them older) who organized to resist enforcement of the Stamp Act. Stampmasters, appointed in England but all of them Americans, were tarred and feathered and chased out of town, and their stocks of stamps seized and burned by the Sons of Liberty. Their houses were wrecked, their furniture broken up, and some of them fled several hundred miles from colony to colony, in fear of their lives, only to find that the Sons of Liberty in one colony would inform the Sons of Liberty in another colony of their presence. There was nothing for them to do but resign, making enforcement of the Stamp Act impossible.

Colonel Mercer, a man with whom Tom Jefferson was acquainted, was appointed Stamp Collector, or Stampmaster, for Virginia. His case was typical. He returned from England with his commission in his pocket to find, to his astonishment, that he was being hanged in effigy in Williamsburg. The students of William and Mary College danced around the effigy dangling from a tree. They were joined by back-country men, in town to attend the session of the House of Burgesses. Merchants and planters paraded through the town demanding that the Colonel resign his post. He thought the matter over and asked Governor Fauquier to accept his resignation. The Governor refused. The Colonel then announced that he would not act as Stampmaster of the colony even if his resignation had been refused. On the instant, he was the hero of the crowd. The effigy was pulled down and he was carried through the town on the shoulders of the cheering mob. The Colonel after further thought took ship back again to England immediately, announcing that private business demanded his presence in London.

As for Patrick Henry, there were some close to the Governor who thought that his speech to the House of Burgesses was treasonable. A rumor went about that he would be charged with treason. But soon the Governor heard that the people would never stand for any such charge. He wrote to Colonial Secretary Conway in London that the Virginians regarded Henry as a "noble patriot" and declared "if the least injury was offered to him, they'd stand by him to the last drop of their blood. Some of them muttered betwixt their teeth, 'Let worst come to the worst, we'll call the French to our succor.'"

It was a strange turn of events, for only five years earlier these same Virginians had been at war with France, fighting side by side with the British redcoats.

Thomas Jefferson was twenty-two during the Stamp Act riots, and still studying law under George Wythe. His hero was Patrick Henry, and he was enormously impressed by Henry's oratory. Whenever Henry had to plead a case in the Williamsburg courts or rose to address the House of Burgesses, Jefferson was there, utterly carried away by the power of his words.

Tom began to study oratory himself, and in this he was assisted by Wythe. Wythe established a moot court—that is, a pretense court—before which students argued cases given to them. Several eminent lawyers sat as judges, and the more prominent citizens were present as an audience.

Jefferson, who had bought a book on oratory, tried his powers before this court. But he soon realized that he had neither the voice nor the leaping imagination needed. He argued well but always in a neatly reasoned pattern, proceeding step by step from one premise to another to the final conclusion. No one could knock a hole in his reasoning. But he was unable to work on the emotions of his listeners as Henry did. His voice was well modulated but quiet. After talking for any length of time, it became husky.

"You reason like Socrates, Tom," George Wythe said. "But you are no Cicero. You will never move an audience by sheer oratory. Forget the dramatic effects. Stick to the pen and the powers of your mind, and you will be one of the leading lawyers of the colony."

In 1767, when he was twenty-four years of age, Tom passed his examinations in law and was admitted to the bar of the Colony of Virginia. He opened a small office to practice in Williamsburg. He was wealthy, well known, well respected, but untried as a lawyer. He wanted to be a success as a lawyer, and live off his earnings in the profession rather than off the money he had inherited. But, as with most young lawyers, the first cases that came to him were lost causes or concerned clients who were able to pay very little for his services.

One of these early cases made a deep impression on Tom and recalled the time of his father's death when the slaves had asked him to whom they now belonged. A mulatto slave named Howland called on him to ask him to petition the court to be freed from his master.

"On what grounds do you think you should be freed?" Tom Jefferson asked the man. Shuffling awkwardly in the presence of the elegant young lawyer, Howland told his story. His great-grandmother, he said, was a white woman and his great-grandfather a Negro slave. These two had had an illegitimate child, Howland's grandmother. The church wardens, who had authority in this matter, ruled that this girl should be the slave of the Negro's master until she was thirty-one years of age. But before she was thirty-one, she herself had given birth to a child. This child, Howland's mother, had been sold as a slave to a man named Netherland. When Howland was born he was pronounced the property of Netherland, who owned his mother.

"Mr. Jefferson," said the mulatto, "I am to be a slave until I am thirty-one years of age, as my mother was, my grandmother and my great-grandmother.

I have to pay for whatever offense my great-grandmother committed when she gave birth to a Negro. Mr. Jefferson, I have done nothing wrong myself and I think I should be a free man and not belong to someone else until I am thirty-one. If I marry and have a child before I am thirty-one, that child will be a slave. And that will go on, Mr. Jefferson, forever and ever."

The man could pay little or no money and Tom Jefferson didn't want any. He took the case, reading up the law on the matter back to the year 1705. Netherland hired a lawyer also to assert his right over Howland. The lawyer he hired was George Wythe—Tom Jefferson's former teacher.

Student and professor then faced each other in court. Tom, after reviewing the laws concerning slavery as they applied to the case, referred to a greater law—the law of nature.

"I suppose it will not be pretended," he said addressing the court, "that the mother being a servant, the child would be a servant also, under the law of nature. . . . Under the law of nature all men are born free, everyone comes into the world with a right to his own person, which includes the liberty of moving and using it at his own will. This is what is called personal liberty, and is given him by the Author of nature, because it is necessary for his own sustenance. The reducing of the mother to servitude was a violation of the law of nature; surely then the same law cannot prescribe a continuance of the violation to her issue, and that too without end, for if it extends to any, it must be to every degree of descendants."

In the mouth of Patrick Henry, this would have been a ringing argument. From Jefferson's lips it came quietly, reasonably and sanely . . . and it failed. George Wythe was about to rise to present his case for the defendant but the court cut him short, and, without further discussion, ruled that Howland must remain a slave until he was thirty-one, and that if before then he fathered any children, they also would be slaves.

In the lobby outside the courtroom Jefferson turned in anguish to Wythe. "How can that be?" he cried. "How can such a terrible thing be done? How can the court sustain a law which enslaves one generation after another, so that the penalty of fatherhood is the slavery of the child?"

"Tom," said Wythe, "the law is the law and courts must uphold the law. That is their function. The courts have no authority to change the law but must rule in accordance with it. Your case was lost, as you must have known, before you made your opening plea."

"But the law is a thoroughly bad law," cried Tom. "You know that yourself, Mr. Wythe. Why, you even set your own slaves free, holding slavery contrary to the laws of God . . ." He stopped there, but the inference was plain. Why had his friend George Wythe, who had freed his own slaves, been willing to defend a man who wished to keep another in slavery? The unasked question was not lost on the subtle George Wythe.

"When a lawyer takes a case into court, Tom," he said, "he performs a service by demonstrating to the public the workings of a law to which they have given their sanction. If the law is a bad and an unjust law, then the lawyer brings this forcibly to the attention of the public by demanding that the law be enforced. And so the lawyers may stir the people to change bad laws by which the courts are bound. But the changing of laws is the province of the people through their elected representatives. If courts could change laws at will, then courts would soon become tyrannical and no man would be safe in his person or in his property."

"And yet," said Tom, "there are some rights of men which no court should have the power to take away. One of those rights is a man's personal liberty. Those rights should be put down in plain language and in writing, as sacred so that they can endure unviolated for all time."

Wythe looked at the young lawyer thoughtfully. "Practice law, Tom," he said. "See its workings. Plead your cases at the bar. You will there be better equipped to turn from the interpretation of law to the framing of law, if that is the course you wish to follow."

Thomas Jefferson took George Wythe's advice. He practiced as a lawyer all over the Colony of Virginia, taking cases in fifty-three of the fifty-six counties then in existence.

He defended the great men of the colony and the

lowliest—the sleek, well-fed planters, the gaunt almost illiterate frontiersmen. He traveled hundreds of miles on horseback from court to court, summer and winter, sometimes staying at the plantations of friends, sometimes in a rough cabin in a clearing so recently made in a Virginia forest that the corn was planted by hand among the stumps of felled trees. He liked mingling with the rough pioneers, listening to their stories of how they came to settle in a particular area.

Their riches lay in the little crops they managed to harvest, the little houses they put up from felled trees, and in their sons who helped to work the land and expand the holding. The independence of their lives, their self-reliance, and the way in which they obtained their living directly from the soil made a tremendous impression on Tom Jefferson. The pioneer farmer remained to him, throughout his life, the best type of human being, the person most to be admired. These frontiersmen, with whom Jefferson visited, rarely saw money and they needed it only to buy powder and bullets. Some spoke Gaelic and some German and they were shy in the presence of the learned lawyer who could talk in Latin and Greek, Italian and French as well as English.

They had a profound respect for a man who could write; they considered it a feat beyond their own abilities to take a spoken word and put it down on paper. Sometimes they made the long trek to Williamsburg to see him at his law office about a deed to their lands or about making a legal trade of one piece of property for another. They told him of families who had moved further on into the Blue Ridge Mountains, through the great forests of white oak, wild cherry, hemlock, pine, poplar, and wild walnut.

"More are moving west, Mr. Jefferson, into the Indian country where the French used to be. Good country. Plenty of game and timber and water and good soil," they said. And Tom thought of the many times he had climbed the little mountain, Monticello, with his father and looked at the great empty lands westward. People were moving into them now, but there were more and more stretching hundreds of miles farther and farther west.

He questioned the frontiersmen about the kinds of trees and plants and wild life in the remote regions. They got to know that he liked to be told of these things. He was a queer kind of a lawyer—well read in the law, but interested in whether there were elk in the mountains and whether the red squirrels were seen in the forests each year earlier than the black or gray. He made notes of these things in a little book, and because the pioneers liked him they told him the forest lore. He was never pompous with them, but listened to them man to man, as if they, in their deerskins, were just as good as he in his velvet breeches and coat of best Yorkshire cloth.

While he had been a law student under George

Wythe, Tom visited Shadwell as often as he could and took his beloved sister Jane canoeing on the river or for walks through the woods around.

She never married and looked forward eagerly to these visits from her brother. She studied his lawbooks and debated points of law with him, and they often played violin together. He was never so happy as when he was with his sister, who had begged that they should never be separated.

Then, in 1765, the year of the Stamp Act, Jane Jefferson died. Tom was inconsolable. He talked to no one for days, would not study or read, but went off by himself into the woods, returning to Shadwell at nighttime without a word to anybody. The pain of Jane's death was never eased. Fifty years later, he would talk about Jane as if she had died only the day before. He carried his grief to the end of his life, a heavy cross he could share with no one, for no one felt about Jane as he had. Yet his work had to go on. Grief could not rule his life. He returned to the task of living.

Visiting one plantation house after another, Jefferson became interested in architecture. He had a natural sense of grace when applied to building and had been shocked as a student by the appearance of William and Mary College in Williamsburg.

The planters' mansions he found little better. They were built for utility in the first instance—close to the river and wharves where the ships docked. They commanded no great views, were often of wood and designed by their owners, who had little or no training in architecture.

Shadwell was like these houses—ample and graceless, a large box surrounded by smaller boxes where the servants and slaves lived. He decided to build a new and more graceful residence and break away from the old habit of building on low-lying ground near a river's edge. He would build his mansion on a mountaintop, so as to be able to see across the valleys and forests to the Blue Ridge Mountains, and be above the low-lying clouds of winter.

The mountain he chose was the one he loved—the one he climbed time and again with his father as a boy, and scores of times later with Jane. He called the mountain Monticello, Italian for "Little Mountain," and when he thought of building a house on it, decided that the house would be called the Hermitage. But a little later he decided to call the house, too, Monticello.

Thomas Jefferson started work on Monticello two years after Jane died. He first drew up his plans, having studied several books on architecture. There were no real architects in Virginia at the time. He had then to be his own architect and master builder.

The plans drawn, he began to calculate the number of bricks required for the mansion, the quantity of lumber, sand and cement and glass that would be needed for the splendid mansion he had in mind.

He had soon agreed with a local contractor to level 250 square feet on the mountaintop for the house site.

Money was short in the colony, and for the work, the contractor got 180 bushels of wheat and 24 bushels of corn—something less than a bushel of grain for every square foot of land leveled. The glass for windows, he ordered from England, the carpet for his dining room from Scotland. He went beyond the normal building requirements, ordering statuary and paintings from Italy. Actual building started in 1769 on one of the wings or out-chambers, as they were called, of the mansion. It was just as well that the start was made, for in February, 1770, old wooden Shadwell burned to the ground.

The fire was disastrous, its cause unknown. All of Tom Jefferson's library, collected from the earliest days, was destroyed in the fire as well as his notes and briefs on a number of law cases. The only books that survived were one or two that were lent to friends.

The servants, knowing his love of music, got his violin out of the burning building along with some of the furniture. But the rest was lost and Tom Jefferson had to move his family into the one wing of Monticello which was nearing completion. Work was pushed from that day on but it was many years before Monticello was finished.

Thomas Jefferson started Monticello as a subject of King George III. He was to finish it as one of the most prominent citizens of a country as yet unheard of— the United States of America.

9

While he was a law student with George Wythe, Thomas Jefferson had fallen in love with Rebecca Burwell, daughter of Lewis Burwell who at times had been acting governor of Virginia. She was the belle of the colony, and tall, lanky Tom Jefferson was so entranced by her that he couldn't keep his mind on his lawbooks. He met her at many dances and social events, spent one rapturous evening dancing with her at a friend's plantation house, but was so shy that although he was determined to propose, he couldn't. He stuttered and mumbled various phrases that conveyed nothing but that he was in love.

Rebecca Burwell married someone else, putting Tom out of his misery. Tom wished her and her bridegroom well, was best man at the wedding, and went back to his books. At twenty-seven he was one of the most eligible bachelors in Virginia, rich in his lands and from his practice of law, and now a member of the House of Burgesses.

He was always welcome wherever he went, and, as a bachelor, constantly invited to dances and parties where the hosts eyed him as a fine catch for their marriageable daughters. Tom liked dancing and playing the violin and singing. He was a good social companion and a good man in the hunting field. But people began to say that he had the makings of a lifelong bachelor. His college friends had all married. Dabney Carr had married Tom's young sister Martha. They lived in a little house with a minimum of furniture and one or two servants and were so happy that Tom envied them. They had a son and doted on him; Tom liked to play with the boy and take him for walks when he visited his sister.

But still he remained a bachelor, never serious about any particular girl after Rebecca Burwell married.

Then Tom Jefferson fell in love with Martha Wayles Skelton. She was the widow of a college friend, Bathurst Skelton. She had been married at seventeen, her husband having died two years later at the age of twenty-four. Tom had known them during their brief marriage and visited their home. He felt sorry for Martha Skelton, a widow at nineteen with a baby son. After her husband's death, she went to live with her father at his plantation called The Forest, at the confluence of the James and the Appomattox rivers.

What was between Tom and Martha at first was a friendship based on sympathy and mutual interest, for Martha Skelton, like Tom's sister Jane, was a good musician. Their relationship turned only slowly to love—but their love was all the stronger for its slow growth. They were married at The Forest on New Year's day, 1772. Martha was twenty-three and Tom twenty-nine. The wedding festivities continued at The Forest until January 18, for the whole of Virginia society gathered there to congratulate the bride and groom. Then the two left for Monticello. Snow was falling and continued to fall heavily until the light carriage in which they were traveling could go no farther. Tom got out, unharnessed the horses, and bride and groom continued on horseback to their home. The snow was as much as two feet deep and they were several hours on their way. When they arrived, it was so late at night that the fires were all out and the servants long in bed.

It wasn't much of a homecoming for the bride. But for Tom Jefferson the months that followed were the happiest in his life. With Martha he started laying out plants for his garden and supervised the building that was still going on. The two went to Williamsburg where Tom had cases to attend to, besides sessions of the House of Burgesses. Their first child, a daughter, was born on September 27, 1772. Jefferson believed that he had at last achieved what he had wished for all his life—a good home, peace, and a family. But over the mountains to the north, storm clouds were gathering which would separate Thomas Jefferson and his wife and deny him the family life for which he longed for many years.

The Stamp Act riots were followed by a refusal of the American colonies to buy any goods, other than the greatest necessities, from England. The result was widespread unemployment in England, many merchants engaged in the American trade going bankrupt. To conciliate the colonies, the Stamp Act was repealed. But before it was repealed, Parliament passed another measure—the Declaratory Act. This asserted the right of Parliament to tax the people of the American (and other) colonies. The repeal of the Stamp Act was celebrated with bonfires and firework displays in all the thirteen colonies. Tom Jefferson and Martha attended a big ball in Williamsburg given to mark the repeal. But, talking matters over later with his friends Dabney Carr, John Page, and Patrick Henry, Tom was disturbed about the Declaratory Act, which boldly asserted the right of the British Parliament to tax the people of the colonies.

"We dance and have our bonfires," he said, "but the problem is not solved. In fact, it is made worse. There might have been some doubt before of Britain's right to tax us. Now that doubt is set aside by the Declaratory Act. By this act we have thrust upon us what we cannot accept—taxation without representation."

Governor Francis Fauquier had died in 1768, and was now replaced by a new governor, Norbone Berkeley, Baron de Botetourt. He was a large man, member of an ancient Norman-English family. Some of his kinsmen had settled in Virginia, so he had some blood ties with the colony. He was well received in Virginia, where the people thought they would be able to get along with him quite as well as they had with Fauquier. He summoned the Burgesses to a meeting at the Governor's mansion, and Tom Jefferson, newly sworn in as a member of the House, listened to his speech delivered in a slow voice with many pauses. Some of the things the Governor had to say hinted at trouble.

Clad in a handsome red coat interworked with gold thread, and white breeches and stockings, the Governor looked the Burgesses over and said, "I have nothing to ask but that you consider well, and follow exactly, without passion or prejudice, the real interests of those you have the honor to represent. They are most certainly consistent with the prosperity of Great Britain, and so they will forever be found when pursued with temper and moderation."

When after paying their respects to the new Governor the House met to consider its business, it was soon found that the interests of the people did not consist in submitting to being taxed by Britain's Parliament. Patrick Henry's famous resolves became immediately part of the business of the House. Tom Jefferson was appointed to a Committee of Propositions and Grievances, and that committee had soon drawn up a number of resolves which were to shake the complacency and bland sentiments of Governor Botetourt.

The first resolution expressed the opinion that the "sole right of imposing taxes on the inhabitants of this, His Majesty's colony and dominion of Virginia, is now, and ever had been, legally and constitutionally vested in the House of Burgesses . . ."

The second asserted the right of the people of Virginia to petition the King directly for redress of their grievances.

The third denied the right of Britain to demand that Virginians accused of treason be taken to England and tried in English courts.

These resolutions were passed by the full House of Burgesses and copies were sent to the legislatures of the other colonies. The effect could have been anticipated. Governor Botetourt summoned the Burgesses to his mansion and said solemnly in that slow voice of his, "Mr. Speaker and Gentlemen of the House of Burgesses, I have heard of your resolves and augur ill of their effect. You have made it my duty to dissolve you; and you are dissolved accordingly."

The effect of being dissolved was that the business of the colony's government could not be carried on. There was a hurried discussion. The Burgesses agreed that they would meet in the house of Mr. Anthony

Hay, who was one of their number, and go on with their proceedings there. The members of the House of Burgesses formed themselves into an association or shadow government for the colony, and decided to ban the importation from England of any article on which a tax had to be paid. The list of articles thus banned included meat, wines, liquor, paper, clothing, and leather.

George Washington presented this resolve to the members of the association. It was adopted unanimously.

But still no one had any thought of disloyalty to the King. All believed that in defending their own rights they were defending the rights of Englishmen as well. When their meeting broke up they drank toasts to King George, to the Queen, and to Governor Botetourt who, in dissolving them, had merely done his duty. They later invited him to a big ball and treated him with every courtesy. But while the fiddlers played and the ladies and gentlemen, led by the Governor, danced their minuets under the glittering chandeliers, the Governor noted that the guests were no longer clad in the rich clothes of English merchants. They were wearing dresses and suits made of Virginia homespun. In the splendor of the ballroom the contest between King and colonies was being politely but firmly waged.

The decision not to buy English goods on which Britain levied any tax was taken not only in Virginia but in most of the other colonies as well. It resulted in the colonists' having to produce themselves many of the articles they had previously imported. Jefferson was delighted, for here was a direct challenge to his ingenuity. He began immediately the planting of grapevines, importing cuttings from Europe, which he gave to his friends. It might be possible, he thought, to produce a Virginia wine which would be a substitute for the Madeira, widely consumed among the gentry, which had to be imported from English merchants on British ships.

He also obtained a large quantity of clover seed to improve his pastures. Good grass would be important now that salted beef was not to be had from England. He encouraged his neighbors not to kill any lambs but to allow them to grow to sheep, for there would be a great need of wool in the colonies in the months and years ahead. He had become increasingly concerned that Virginia was a one-crop colony. If tobacco prices went down, then Virginia's whole economy would be wrecked. He wanted to see a variety of crops in the colony, particularly since the old tobacco lands were beginning to yield poorer and poorer harvests as the soil was leached of nourishment. He experimented with alfalfa and gave some seed to George Washington to plant on his estate at Mount Vernon. However, the plant, excellent for hay, did not flourish in the acid Virginia soil.

The decision not to import English goods on which a tax had to be paid was taken in the spring of 1769. Its effect in England was immediate. English merchants, who made millions of pounds a year out of trade with America, found their profits wiped out. They began to clamor to Parliament to lift the tax on the articles exported to America. Parliament was forced to oblige. In November of 1769 Governor Botetourt summoned the House of Burgesses into session. He was in a good mood, for he had excellent news for the colonists. He assured them that the government had no intention whatever of laying any further taxes on the colonies, and that at the next session of Parliament the taxes on paper, glass, and paint would be removed.

"They're coming to their senses," said Dabney Carr. "We have struck them where it hurts—in the purse."

Jefferson shook his head. "There's still the Declaratory Act, Dabney," he said. "That act gives the Parliament of Britain the power to tax us any time it wishes. Until that is removed we are utterly at their mercy."

"But, Tom," said Dabney, "if, after all, they remove taxes against which we protest, what is there to worry about? They propose a tax, we object strenuously; we gain our point. Surely, that is the way things should work."

"Dabney," said Tom seriously, "we commit a grave error if we neglect principles and are misled by particular cases. Always search for the principle. The principle is that we should not be taxed without direct representation in the British Parliament. Until that principle is firmly established and acknowledged, we are at the mercy of any ministry that comes into power in England."

There now began to be formed in the House of Burgesses a party of the younger members, led by Patrick Henry and including Tom Jefferson, Dabney Carr, Richard Henry Lee, and Francis L. Lee. They were the active, thrusting members, bold in their opposition to arbitrary British rule.

The older members—Peyton Randolph, Colonel Bland, and George Wythe—also opposed the arbitrary rule of Britain. But they believed that the best way to obtain their ends was by giving no unneeded offense to Britain. They were all for form and etiquette and polite protest, delivered through established channels. Basically, nothing divided these two parties. They were divided only on method—the one advocating a bold stand; the other a more gentlemanly approach.

Richard Henry Lee was a man Tom Jefferson greatly respected. In his first speech to the House of Burgesses, as a new member eleven years previously, he had spoken strongly against slavery, and proposed that it be abolished gradually, a first step being a heavy tax on the importation of new slaves into the colony. He was hopelessly defeated.

Tom Jefferson was haunted by the continuance of the slave trade. He never got over the pathetic questions of the slaves asking to whom they belonged when his father died. He never forgot the case of Howell, condemned to slavery for the deeds of his great-grandmother. At the first meeting of the House of Burgesses, before it was dissolved, Tom worked on a bill to improve the condition of slaves. The bill was voted down.

"I tremble for the fate of my country when I reflect that God is just," Jefferson cried bitterly when he found all his efforts to help the slaves defeated. As the law stood in Virginia at that time, a county court could order a slave to be hacked to pieces if he persisted in going about in the night or running away. Jefferson could not even get this terrible punishment taken off the statute books.

10

For the next two years, the political crisis in the colonies dwindled. The British government, rebuffed by the Stamp Act riots and injured by the refusal of Americans to buy any goods on which a tax had to be paid, decided to do nothing for a while. Many of the taxes were rescinded; Americans started importing again, and although a tax remained on tea (which was drunk in the American colonies in copious amounts), few Americans bought any tea but that which was smuggled in by the Dutch with the connivance of New England merchants.

Tom Jefferson continued with his law practice, which was building up very rapidly. He sent to England to order a dozen or more books on the theory of government, for as a member of the House of Burgesses his interest in government was keenly aroused. He worked on the building of Monticello, making detailed notes of how much earth a man could carry in a two-wheel barrow as opposed to a one-wheel barrow. He became an efficiency engineer before the term had ever been thought of.

Tom's plans for Monticello were the talk of the country. No such private building had ever been erected. It contained many novelties, among them a compass on the roof of Jefferson's study with a pointer connected to the weathercock above and outside. Tom didn't always want to go out of doors to see which way the wind was blowing. He kept notes on wind direction and strength and tried to relate these to the weather to be expected. He planned service elevators to save his staff from running up and down stairs with trays, and also a double-faced clock, one face on the outside of the house so that the one clock told time for those inside Monticello and those out in the garden and fields around. He was always inventing something to cut down work or promote convenience.

His fame as an architect was such that the new Governor of Virginia, Lord Dunmore, asked him to draw up a plan for an addition to the College of William and Mary, which he did.

Virginia was not as fortunate in Lord Dunmore as it had been in Fauquier and the Baron of Botetourt. Lord Botetourt had died in 1770, and was succeeded by Lord Dunmore in 1771, William Nelson of Yorktown acting as governor in the interim.

Dunmore had been Governor of New York before coming to Virginia, and some ugly stories about him reached the colony. One night a number of drunken rioters attacked the coach of the Chief Justice in the streets. The coach was wrecked and the tails cut off the horses. The Chief Justice offered a reward of two hundred pounds for the capture of his assailants. All New York laughed at the affair. It was an open secret that Dunmore himself had led the gang that attacked the coach.

He was a small man, but strong and healthy, with a quick temper and uncertain manners. He was not likely to suit the elegant Virginians who, though they opposed Botetourt politically, admired him enough to erect a statue to him after his death.

Lord Dunmore was almost a year and a half in the colony before he summoned the House of Burgesses into session. They were summoned when it was discovered that several clever forgeries had been foisted on the colonial treasurer and the credit of the colony was shaken. They were, Dunmore said, to discuss this matter. But the Virginians, with Jefferson to the fore, had something else to discuss—a development which had not taken place in Virginia, but far away to the north in Narragansett Bay, Rhode Island.

Beset by taxes and artificially raised prices, the merchants of New England had turned to smuggling, which had become a respectable and indeed a patriotic trade. Britain had many years earlier passed a series of navigation acts demanding that all goods bound for sale in the American colonies were to be carried in British ships. This restriction on their supplies didn't sit at all well with the New Englanders. They took to smuggling goods ashore from foreign ships, or sending ships of their own to foreign ports—particularly the French and Dutch West Indies, to bring back goods which were landed without payment of duties.

Tea was smuggled into the colonies in huge quantities by the Dutch and the customs officials could do little to stop the trade. Men of such eminence as John Hancock were known to be deeply engaged in the smuggling business. But they did not think of themselves as smugglers, but as free traders, performing a very necessary service in the interests of their countrymen—and to their own profit.

Britain still needed to raise money in America but had found that taxation brought nothing but trouble. It was decided then to clamp down on smuggling. If the smugglers could be stamped out there would be a great increase in the revenue obtained through customs. Admiralty courts were appointed to try anyone arrested for smuggling. Trials were conducted by naval officers, without a jury. Sentence often resulted in the confiscation of all property owned by the defendant. Side by side with this, revenue cutters and schooners staffed by British naval officers started prowling the New England coasts looking for smugglers and their secret warehouses. Among these naval officers was Lieutenant Dudlington of the schooner *Gaspee.*

Dudlington was a real fire-eater—a "blind-your-eyes" naval officer of the worst type. He was merciless in boarding and impounding fishing vessels on charges of smuggling. He also raided farms and stole sheep and cut down fruit trees. He was indeed so heartily hated that there was talk of fitting out an armed vessel to blow him and the *Gaspee* out of the water.

As matters turned out, that was not necessary. While chasing a smuggler up Narragansett Bay, the *Gaspee* ran aground on a sand bank—enticed over the bank by the smuggler, who knew the local waters well. There the vessel lay waiting for a tide to float it off. At midnight a group of American seamen and fishermen from Providence, who had had enough of Lieutenant Dudlington, set out in boats, boarded the *Gaspee,* seriously wounded Dudlington, and burned his schooner to the waterline.

An attack had been made on a vessel of the Royal Navy and Britain could not ignore it. A special court of inquiry was established in Providence with power to send any suspected of taking part in the burning of the *Gaspee* to England for trial.

This was the news that troubled Jefferson, Henry, Peyton Randolph, George Wythe, and others as they gathered in Williamsburg to attend the session of the House of Burgesses summoned by Governor Dunmore. Taking Americans to England for trial was without precedent in the history of the colonies. A gross violation of constitutional right was involved, for basic law gave every man the right to a trial before his peers—by which is meant his equals; those who shared his way of living. An American could not expect to find his peers in England. Furthermore, he would be put to the impossible expense of paying the travel of witnesses from America to London to testify on his behalf. And English courts would not be well disposed to an American "smuggler."

The older members of the House of Burgesses shared Tom Jefferson's view that the whole procedure was illegal and tyrannical. But as always, they were inclined to make whatever protest was called for with caution and politeness, so as not to offend the London government further.

That, however, did not suit Tom Jefferson. The issue was critical and the time for courtesy in protecting the basic rights of Americans was long past. He canvassed Patrick Henry, Richard Henry Lee, Francis L. Lee, and his boyhood friend Dabney Carr. They agreed that a direct and positive action must be taken, and met in a private room of the Raleigh Tavern to talk the matter over. The meeting lasted a long time. In public Patrick Henry was a great orator, but he indulged in no oratory in these small gatherings, bringing his shrewd mind efficiently to work. He had the least legal training of all the men present. But he had the gift of getting immediately to the crux of any situation.

"What is threatened in Rhode Island," he said, "is threatened in every one of the thirteen colonies. We get assurances that Rhode Island is a special case, and that the same thing would not happen here in Virginia. But it will happen here if the King or his ministers wish it to happen. So we must take the view that anything of this sort that happens in any other colony is the immediate business of Virginia."

"That is why we are meeting here," said Jefferson quietly. "We are Virginians, discussing Rhode Island business because it is our business also."

"The big trouble is that we only learn what has happened weeks later and we get only one side of the story—the government's side," said Dabney Carr. "Everything we learn officially we learn through a newspaper which can be suspended by the Governor. If the newspaper gave any other point of view, it would be closed down and the printer would lose his business."

"It should be possible to start another newspaper, without any connection with the government," said Richard Henry Lee.

Jefferson shook his head. "The governor of any colony can close down a newspaper any time he wants," he said. "He has the right. And he will use it. Some other method of keeping in touch with what is happening in our neighboring colonies is needed."

The discussion went on, and out of it came a decision to appoint a Committee of Correspondence, whose job it would be to obtain accurate news of any happenings in the neighboring colonies or in Britain affecting Americans. A resolution to establish such a committee was drawn up. The resolution also instructed the Committee of Correspondence to inquire into affairs in Rhode Island and find out on what authority a special court in Rhode Island was appointed with power to transport Americans accused of offenses for trial "in places beyond the seas."

When this was agreed, there came the matter of getting the assent of the older members of the House of Burgesses to the resolution. It was proposed that some of them should be appointed to the Committee of Correspondence, which would give them a share in its work and control of its activities. And it was further proposed that the resolution should be so framed that it would appear to be a move to maintain order in the colony and prevent wild and inflammatory rumors going about. Then the meeting broke up. But as Thomas Jefferson left the Raleigh Tavern that night he recalled his conversation with George Wythe many years ago. Wythe had said that there were two sources of government in society—the tavern and the official legislature, and that the tavern was often the superior body. It seemed that what wise George Wythe had said was likely to prove true. The little meeting in the Raleigh Tavern might prove more important than any meeting in the House of Burgesses.

The next day at the meeting of the House of Burgesses a number of minor matters were brought up for attention. An addition was voted to the house of the public jailer. Some new ferries across the river were agreed upon. The hours went by, filled with the essential trivia of colonial government. Then, when local matters had been settled, the Burgesses turned to consider the state of the colony as a whole.

Dabney Carr, having obtained the consent of the Speaker, rose to address the House. The older members looked at him tolerantly. He was to make his maiden speech. They remembered how nervous they had felt when they had first risen to address the House, and smiled encouragement to him. The matter would hardly be an important one, though they had heard rumors of a meeting of the younger members at the Raleigh the night before.

In a firm, well-modulated voice, without a trace of nervousness, Carr began his preliminary remarks. It was the duty of all, he said, to uphold the King's peace; to put down rumors and wild reports which inflamed people against the government on false grounds. These were days when many things were happening, and the need for accurate news of these events, particularly when they affected the people of Virginia, was therefore critical. To achieve this end, with which he was sure no member of the House could take issue, he wished to offer a number of resolutions.

He then moved the resolutions concerning a Committee of Correspondence agreed upon the night before. These resolutions had been carefully worded, largely through the skill of Jefferson, in such a manner that to object to them would appear to be on the side of disorder. The resolutions passed the House without a single dissenting vote. The Committee of Correspondence was formed, and named to it were Peyton Randolph, Speaker of the House; the grave Robert Carter Nicholas, an eminent and greatly respected clergyman; Richard Bland, he of the parchment-like cheeks who was such a great authority on law; and together with these older members, Patrick Henry, Dabney Carr, Dudley Digges, an old school friend of Jefferson, and Jefferson himself.

In all, there were eleven members of the committee and any six of them had authority to carry out the committee's business. A letter was sent to the legislatures of the other colonies informing them of the action and suggesting they follow suit. The other colonies very shortly did so. From now on they would not be divided. A net of communication would draw them together. They would not allow themselves to be deceived any further by official propaganda but would establish the facts of any case for themselves.

Governor Dunmore did what was anticipated. He dissolved the House of Burgesses at the earliest possible moment. He could not do this right away, because of the skill with which the resolutions had been worded. But he dismissed the Burgesses eleven days later with the pious recommendation that in future they try to abolish gambling in Virginia and substitute for it "a love of agriculture and attention to . . . private affairs, by which you will render a most essential service . . ."

Dunmore had made himself unpopular with the Virginians even before his arrival in the colony as governor. When he was appointed, he delayed several months in New York, implying that he hated to leave the delights of New York and its superior culture for the rural simplicity of Virginia.

He had sent a deputy in his stead, but the Virginians had refused to pay the salary of this deputy and they had made their refusal good. Nonetheless they were gentlemen, and when the Governor did arrive, they extended to Dunmore all the courtesies they had given their previous governors, Fauquier and Botetourt, whom they had liked. They gave balls for him, invited him to hunts, attended on him at the Governor's mansion, and indeed a kind of court circle grew up around Dunmore, the wealthy planters' wives vying for precedence in being seated at the Governor's table. Dunmore used this social rivalry to build what he hoped would be a circle of supporters around him—friends of the Governor and therefore of the King. Virginians were not disloyal to the King at this time. They considered him to be the victim of his ministers, sympathized with him, and heartily drank his health. The awakening was to come later.

Lord Dunmore made an especial point of cultivating the most prominent of the Virginians—George Washington. Whenever Washington arrived at Williamsburg he was invited to dine with the Governor. At formal banquets Washington was given the place of highest honor. Dunmore even consulted Washington about a journey through the colony, but Washington was unable to make the tour because of the death of his stepdaughter.

Washington had been among the members who heartily supported the Committee of Correspondence originated by Jefferson and his young friends. Tom Jefferson held him in the greatest respect. Washington was eleven years older than Thomas Jefferson—forty-one at the time the Committee of Correspondence was formed. But in those eleven years lay a tremendous difference between the two. Washington had been old enough to serve in the French and Indian Wars, had been on the staff of General Braddock, had had all the Virginia troops under his command and led them with great personal courage and brilliance. In all this time, Tom had been just a law student.

Washington was a figure of awe for Tom Jefferson, who called him, as everyone did, Colonel Washington. They had, however, many things in common. They loved riding and horses and were fastidious about their mounts. When Jefferson had a horse brought to him to ride, he would pass a cambric handkerchief over its glistening neck. If the handkerchief was soiled, he sent the horse back for further grooming. Washington was equally critical of horses. A gentleman rode a good horse, excellently groomed; on that there was no compromise.

The two were equally interested in agriculture, Washington anxious to improve the productivity of his land at Mount Vernon. They were together in opposing encroachment on their rights as Americans. But here Jefferson, with his legal training and his wide reading of philosophers like Locke and Montesquieu, was more forward. The older man was cool, level-headed, but firm. He stood on a middle ground between the conservatism of the old Tidewater aristocracy and the fiery patriotism of Patrick Henry. He was not much swayed by eloquence, did not speak much in the House of Burgesses, for he had no ability as an orator. But Tom Jefferson, attending meetings, often watched Washington sitting a head higher than the others around him, silent, grave, attentive, deeply courteous. It seemed to Tom that here was a kind of a rock around which the issues of the debate swirled without outward affect; a rock of such strength that when the storm subsided, it alone would dominate the scene, unflinching and unchanged in principle and purpose.

11

Thirty-five days after he moved the formation of a Committee of Correspondence, Dabney Carr died of fever. Tom was in Williamsburg when his friend died and rushed back to find that he had already been buried. He remembered how only fifteen years before they had studied Latin and Greek together under the old oak tree. He recalled the mutual pledge they had made, that whoever died first the other would bury him under this oak. And so he had his friend's body disinterred and laid to rest under the oak tree as he had promised.

He looked into Dabney's affairs and found that he had left an estate valued at only a little over £1,000. He had been very happy in his little house with his six children and a minimum of furniture, and wanted nothing more. Whatever spare money he had, he spent on books, for he had over two hundred volumes in his library.

"You are to come and stay with me," Tom told Dabney's widow, his sister Martha. "Bring all the children. They will be my children now. I will not have it any other way." He took his sister and her six children into his house at Monticello, and brought them up at his own expense as if he were their father, so that he was surrounded by their love all his life. He found time to take the older ones for horseback rides and walks in the woods, taught them how to manage a canoe, and scolded them if they were lazy at their lessons.

The death of Dabney Carr gave Tom Jefferson, at the age of thirty, a family of eight children. There was his own infant daughter, his wife's son by her first marriage, and Dabney's six children. He loved to hear their voices in the woods and around the house. When he was studying the children were supposed to be quiet or play away from the area of his study. But sometimes they interrupted him and he would get up from his desk, irritated, to tell them to be quiet. But he could never be really stern with them and he would forget his books for a while and lift them up on his shoulders, the little ones screaming in fear and delight to be raised high off the ground to the tall shoulders of Tom Jefferson.

Jefferson spent the next several months after the death of Dabney Carr at Monticello with his greatly enlarged family. He was there through the autumn and winter of 1773-1774, kept in touch through the Committee of Correspondence and the visits of his friends with what was happening in the other colonies and in England.

He did a great deal of work supervising the building of his mansion, still under construction, and laying out the gardens around. And he spent many hours a day also in reading. He had read widely in law and in the classics in his youth. He read now in history and in theories of government.

The tomes he delved in were dull for others; for the questing mind of Tom Jefferson they were vital and full of interest. He read Kames's *Historical Law Tracts and History of Property*, Dalrymple's *Essay Towards a General History of Feudal Property in Great Britain*, and Wilson's *Considerations of the Nature and Extent of the Legislative Authority of the British Parliament*.

When he came upon a passage that particularly appealed to him, he copied it out in his Commonplace Book. One of the extracts he made became a key principle in his thinking. It was from Kames's *History of Property* and read:

★ 133 ★

The perfection of human society consists in that just degree of union among the individuals, which to each reserves freedom and independency as far as is consistent with peace and order. The bonds of society where every man shall be bound to dedicate the whole of his industry to the common interest would be of the strictest kind, but it would be unnatural and uncomfortable because destructive of liberty and independency.

The wording is old-fashioned and obscures the meaning today. But the sense remains unshaken. Good government reserves the greatest possible amount of freedom to individuals. A government that demands that all that men produce be dedicated to the state (as for instance Communism) is unnatural because it destroys individual liberty.

When Tom Jefferson made this entry in his Commonplace Book he was not thinking of communism, however. He was thinking of Britain's restraint on the trade of the American colonies for the benefit of England; on the many taxes Americans had to pay, again for the benefit of England; and on the power to tax Americans without representation which the British Parliament had asserted. It seemed to him that too much of the American effort went to support the English government. Liberty and independency were threatened. He determined to challenge that threat and challenge it boldly.

While he was studying his books and formulating

his ideas, an event occurred in Boston which brought the whole crisis to a head. The East India Company of Britain was in a ruinous state. One of its principal commodities was tea, but thousands of chests of tea remained unsold in the London warehouses because the price was too high. Americans were tremendous tea drinkers—so much so that travelers remarked that many American women would sooner give up their dinners than miss a "dish of tea." But they got their tea cheaply from merchants who obtained it from Dutch smugglers. The East India Company could not compete with the price of smuggled tea and all attempts to stop the smuggling failed.

To save the East India Company from ruin, the British government decided that its surplus tea should be exported to America and sold so cheaply there that even the smugglers could not compete with the price. It would sell at ten shillings a pound instead of twenty shillings a pound, a price so cheap as to be unheard of. There was a catch, however. Three pennies of the ten shillings a pound that the Americans would be paying for their bargain tea would be a tax. In buying the tea they would be admitting the right of Britain to tax them.

Lord North, the British Prime Minister, was quite sure, however, that Americans would put price before principle—their appetite for tea was such that they would buy up the cheap tea quickly, ignoring the tiny tax.

The tea ships sailed to New York, Philadelphia,

Charleston, and Boston. But nobody bid on their cargoes. Lord North was wrong—Americans were not going to pay a tax, even on bargain-price tea. Not a single chest of tea was bought by an American merchant. Worse, in Boston, a band of patriots dressed as Indians (some merely threw a blanket over their shoulders and wiped a little soot on their faces) boarded the tea ships and emptied all the tea chests into the harbor.

The gesture was one of defiance and the use of an Indian disguise one of sarcasm. When Britain had first proposed to tax the colonies under the Stamp Act, it was asserted that the money was needed to protect them from the threat of the French and the Indians. There hadn't been a warlike Indian in Massachusetts in a hundred years. So the Bostonians produced some warlike "Indians" as a jibe at the pretensions of the British government.

Other "tea parties" followed that held at Boston. New York and New Jersey "braves" flung chests of tea into the sea. Tea drinking became such a sign of treason to the American cause that not a dish of tea was to be had in any house in America. Americans turned from tea drinking to coffee drinking, becoming and remaining the world's greatest coffee drinkers.

The reaction in England was swift and angry. Demands came from all sides that the "rebels" be punished—and terribly punished. But the British government, having found it had made a mistake in taxing all the colonies, thus uniting them, decided not to make that union firmer by punishing all the colonies. In fact they wouldn't even punish any colony. They would punish instead a single town—the town of Boston. They closed the port. No goods could be brought into it. No goods could be sent out of it. Boston was doomed to die a lingering death.

Tom Jefferson, George Washington, Patrick Henry, Richard Henry Lee—all the prominent Virginians heard of the Boston Tea Party through the Committee of Correspondence shortly after it occurred, December 16, 1773. When they gathered the following spring to meet in the House of Burgesses in Williamsburg, they wondered what action, if any, Britain would take. Meantime they went on with the business of the government of Virginia. Then, in the midst of their orderly deliberations, a messenger arrived at the door and a sealed paper was hurriedly passed to the Speaker, Peyton Randolph. The debate stopped. All eyes turned to Randolph. He asked permission to interrupt the business of the House and broke the seal. His face went white as he read the paper.

"Gentlemen," he cried, "I have grave news. By act of Parliament, the Port of Boston in the Colony of Massachusetts is to be utterly closed; the closure to go into effect on June 1."

The business of the House of Burgesses was immediately suspended while the import of this news was considered. All were horrified by Britain's brutality in declaring economic war on a single American town. But after the first reaction there was the usual division over whether to lodge a courteous but firm protest or make an outright denunciation in strong terms of Britain's act.

Some argued that Boston was run by mobs anyway—it was a town of turmoil. What happened in Boston was to some degree the fault of the people of Boston—their eagerness to resort to riot against any measure with which they did not agree. What had happened to Boston would not necessarily happen to Williamsburg or any other town of the colonies.

But Patrick Henry saw in the vengeance on Boston a threat to all the colonies. Virginians should feel about Boston, he said, exactly the same sense of outrage as if the James River had been blocked off and no tobacco allowed to be shipped down it for the English market. George Washington agreed with Patrick Henry. The question was, he said, whether Americans should "supinely sit and see one province after another fall a prey to despotism."

Despotism? It was a strong word for so level-headed a man as Washington to use. It made the more conservative members think again.

Jefferson knew that there was danger in this division between young and old members. They must be brought together. A protest must be made on behalf of Boston, and it must be a protest which would be dramatic and yet have the full support of the whole House of Burgesses.

It was up to the younger members to take the lead, but in doing so not to leave the older members behind. Jefferson, Patrick Henry, Richard Henry Lee, Francis L. Lee, and several others met in the council room of the House of Burgesses where they had a whole library of lawbooks at their disposal. Jefferson was now the strategist, the man who had to unite the fire of Henry with the conservatism of the older members in an effective protest. The plan he proposed was brilliant. The whole of Virginia, he urged, should unite in a day of solemn mourning, prayer, and fasting on June 1 when the port of Boston was closed. No business should be transacted; special religious services should be held and sermons preached in every hamlet; and people should appear in mourning clothing. The object of the day should be to "implore Heaven to avert from us the evils of civil war, to inspire us with firmness in the support of our rights, and to turn the hearts of the King and Parliament to moderation and justice."

A resolution to this effect was agreed upon and drawn up and to give it greater emphasis it was proposed that the grave Robert Carter Nicholas, a man revered for his religious feeling throughout Virginia, should move the resolution before the whole of the House of Burgesses. Coming from Mr. Carter, none would vote against it.

The resolution was moved. On the first of June, the day of fasting and prayer was observed. Its effect was tremendous. Everyone knew the reason for the observance of this day. Everyone, in doing so, placed himself solidly in support of the people of Boston. And everyone, hearing the proclamation read from pulpit after pulpit, with its reference to the "evils of civil war," was made aware of how grave were the issues which suddenly loomed before Americans.

Lord Dunmore, of course, had to take action. As soon as the House of Burgesses had passed the resolution calling for the day of prayer, he summoned the Burgesses to the Governor's mansion.

"Mr. Speaker and Gentlemen of the House of Burgesses," he said, "I have in my hand a paper published by order of your House, conceived in such terms as reflect highly upon His Majesty and the Parliament of Great Britain, which makes it necessary for me to dissolve you and you are dissolved accordingly." When he had done, he glanced for a moment at George Washington. Washington had been Dunmore's guest at dinner only a few days previously. But Washington had heartily subscribed to the resolution which made it necessary for the Governor to dissolve the House of Burgesses. They stared at each other coldly, and then Washington, with a perfunctory bow, turned his back and trooped out of the Governor's mansion with the rest of the members.

The Virginians were not finished with their business, however. They retired to what was becoming their other house of legislature—the Raleigh Tavern and met in the Apollo room. There they agreed without a dissenting vote that an attack on any colony would be regarded as an attack on all.

They decided to write to the Committee of Correspondence in the other colonies proposing that delegates be sent to a meeting in some central city to discuss the state of all the colonies and decide on a united policy. What they were suggesting was an unofficial government which would direct American policies in future disputes with King and Parliament— a government of all the colonies. The meetings of the delegates of this elected but unofficial government were to be called a Congress. It was a first step toward independence, but even those who drew up the resolution were unaware of this. What resulted was the first meeting of the Continental Congress, held in Philadelphia in September 1774, the body that was to become the Congress of the United States of America.

Events were moving fast and toward a crisis. But the size of that crisis and the swiftness of that movement was still unsuspected. Tom Jefferson returned to Monticello deep in thought.

☆ ☆ ☆ ☆ ☆ ☆ ☆ ☆ ☆ ☆ ☆

12

Back at Monticello, Jefferson decided to put on paper his thoughts on the position of the American colonists. Just what authority had the British Parliament to govern them? Just what authority had the King of England over the colonists in America? If he had any authority at all, how had the King come to have that authority? Who had given it to him? Had the people given it to him? Was it part of his right as King? Or was it something he had assumed for himself?

These were the questions that went through Tom

Jefferson's mind as he sat alone in his study night after night in Monticello. To answer them he went back deep into English history, to the original settlement of England by the Angles and Saxons.

These people, under their leaders, had come from the deep dark forests of Germany and made themselves a new home in England. They had immediately started to rule themselves, throwing off the rule of their old chieftains who remained in Germany. The American colonists, Jefferson argued, were in exactly the same position. Their forefathers had left their homeland, England, and settled in a new country. They were no more under the authority of the English King than the old Saxon and Angle immigrants in England were under the rule of the chieftains they had left in Germany.

Jefferson turned to another aspect of the matter. The King of England had for many years been acknowledged as King of the British-Americans in the thirteen colonies. That could not be disputed. But the King of England was also the King of Hanover, which was his ancestral domain. Yet the laws of England did not apply to Hanover, nor the laws of Hanover apply to England.

The same should be true for America. The British Parliament should not have the right to legislate for Americans any more than an American Parliament should have the right to legislate for Englishmen. They might share a king in common, but that was all.

Jefferson put these thoughts down on paper in a

statement soon to be known as "A Summary View of the Rights of British America." Some of the sentences foreshadowed a greater document yet to come.

"Single acts of tyranny," Jefferson wrote, "may be ascribed to the accidental opinion of the day; but a series of oppressions begun at a distinguished period and pursued unalterably through every change of ministers, too plainly prove a deliberate and systematical plan of reducing us to slavery. . . .

"Can any one reason be assigned why 160,000 electors in the island of Great Britain should give law to four millions in the States of America, every individual of whom is equal to every individual of them in virtue, in understanding, and in bodily strength . . . ?

"Let those flatter who fear . . . it is not an American art . . . They know . . . that kings are the servants, not the proprietors of the people."

So Jefferson's document went. And he concluded it with words of warning: "The God who gave us life gave us liberty at the same time: the hand of force may destroy, but cannot disjoin them. That, sire, is our last, our determined resolution."

When his document was written, Tom Jefferson made two copies of it and set out for a convention which had been called in Williamsburg to elect members to the first Continental Congress, among other things. He was determined to present the document to the members of the convention as a guide for themselves and for whatever delegates they sent

to the Congress in Philadelphia. But Tom didn't get
to Williamsburg. On the journey he was stricken with
an attack of dysentery and had to return to Monticello. He sent his two copies on to Williamsburg, one
to Patrick Henry and one to Peyton Randolph.

Henry probably never read his copy. He was, as
Tom Jefferson remarked of him, the laziest man in
the world when it came to reading. He was always going to read something but never got around to it. But
Peyton Randolph read the document at a meeting of
the convention delegates in his house—a packed,
tense meeting of men who knew they had arrived at
a crossroads and feared that one step in the wrong
direction might bring them to ruin. The younger
delegates cheered the document. The older members
agreed with it—but drew back. It was too hasty, too
offensive to the King; "too bold," as one delegate put
it, "for the present state of things."

The convention adopted a much milder set of instructions for their delegates to the Philadelphia
Congress. But Tom's friends had his "Summary View
of the Rights of British America" printed in Williamsburg, and it was not long before copies reached London. One came into the hands of Edmund Burke, an
outspoken Irish member who had frequently criticized
the King's policy. Recently elected to represent the
great English port of Bristol, Burke used Tom Jefferson's document as a club to beat the ministers with
on their attitude to Americans.

Nobody in England had heard of Tom Jefferson

before. Who was this Virginia upstart who dared address the King in such terms? they wondered. Well, they would teach him a lesson, and Jefferson's name was put on a bill by which he, with other American patriots, was to be stripped of all his lands. The bill, however, was never passed by the Parliament.

While the first Continental Congress met in Philadelphia, Jefferson remained at Monticello recovering from his illness and supervising the work on his house. He knew how to be patient and how, in times of anxiety, it was best just to go ahead with routine work that had to be done.

In Philadelphia the delegates met and Patrick Henry found a tendency among them to think of themselves as New Yorkers and Pennsylvanians and Carolinians. He determined to change that attitude. The British army and the British fleet threatened them all, he said, without reference to their boundaries. "The distinction between Virginians, Pennsylvanians, New Yorkers and New Englanders is no more," he cried. "I am not a Virginian, but an American."

An American? People had thought of themselves previously as British Americans. But Henry had used no adjective. He was a plain American, a member of a new people in a new land with the right to govern themselves. They cheered his speech and some of the barriers between the delegates began to dissolve.

And yet the members were not ready for the terrible step that seemed to lie ahead of them wherever they turned—separation from the mother country and her King. They recoiled from it. Britain had been the mother country for well over a century. Were they really to turn their backs upon her and go a separate way? The thought was too dreadful to entertain.

George Washington, who was among the Virginia delegates, made no speeches but listened closely to all that was said. When the Congress adjourned he wrote a friend, "I am well satisfied that no such thing as independence is desired by any thinking man in all North America; on the contrary . . . it is the ardent wish of the warmest advocates of liberty that peace and tranquility on constitutional grounds be restored and the horrors of civil war prevented."

When the first Continental Congress broke up, a declaration of the rights of Americans had been agreed upon, and the old weapon of economic war again produced. It was agreed that after December, Americans would not import any goods from Britain and after September of 1775 they would not export any goods to Britain. These measures had been successful in securing the repeal of the Stamp Act. It was expected that they would now result in the reopening of the Port of Boston and the removal of other grievances, the chief among them being the taxing of the colonies without granting them representation.

Jefferson, at Monticello, went over all the work of the First Continental Congress, in particular the part referring to the importing of goods from England, and was horrified at what he found. The colonies were not all bound equally by the embargo. They had to conform only to those parts of it to which their deputies had agreed. Instead of being united under the Congress, the colonies were permitted to go their own way. Angrily Jefferson quoted part of the Divine Service to illustrate his view of the works of the First Continental Congress. "We have left undone those things which we ought to have done, and have done those things which we ought not to have done," he said. But he did not add, "and there is no health in us."

Soon Jefferson was attending another meeting of the Virginia Convention which had replaced the old House of Burgesses. It was held at St. John's Church, Richmond. There was, as there had always been, the same division among the members—the younger ones now pressing for a break with Britain, the older hoping for reconciliation. It was Patrick Henry again who shattered the hopes of the older members. After a wealth of conciliatory speeches and warnings against going too hastily, Henry got to his feet and hurled a bombshell.

A free government could not exist without a militia, he argued. If Virginia was a free government then it ought to have a militia, and he proposed that the colony be immediately put in a state of defense and a committee appointed to make plans for establishing a militia to protect the colony.

Pandemonium broke loose in the church. A militia? What for? Virginia wasn't threatened. America's friends in the British Parliament were active on her behalf. The King showed some signs of relenting in his attitude. Anyway, where would they get stores and arms and generals and soldiers? Where was the money to be obtained to supply all these things?

Richard Henry Lee, John Page, and George Mason supported Henry. Richard Bland, Benjamin Harrison, and Edmund Pendleton opposed him. Then Jefferson rose and, with quiet reasoning and well-chosen argument, supported Henry. People looked at Washington. He was the soldier among them. What were his views? Washington sat listening but did not utter a word. He knew what war was like. He had seen the whitened bones of men lying in the tangled woods of the Ohio Valley. He'd seen heavily wounded men struggling to keep up with an army for days, only to drop to their deaths and be left unburied in the wilderness. War was bloody and bestial. It was the last resort of free men. He held his peace.

But Henry had not finished. He turned to those who advocated more negotiations with Britain, more resolutions and petitions. "We have petitioned, we have remonstrated, we have supplicated, we have prostrated ourselves before the throne," he cried. ". . . there is no longer any room for hope. If we wish to be free, we must fight. . . . Gentlemen may cry 'Peace! Peace!' but there is no peace. The war has actually begun. . . . Our brethren are already in the field! Why stand we here idle? . . . Is life so dear, or peace so sweet as to be purchased at the price of chains and slavery? I know not what course others may take; but as for me, give me liberty, or give me death!"

He sat down. There was silence in the old church. Liberty or death. Had it come to that?

The resolution to raise a Virginia militia passed by only five votes. The people were not yet ready for war.

13

In England the King's ministers sniffed the wind and caught the scent of gunpowder and ruin.

Large quantities of gunpowder and arms, it was said, had been got together in the colonies to resist the King's authority in open rebellion. Side by side with this, the American decision not to import further goods from Britain threatened the ruin of the powerful merchant class in the mother country. Two steps were plainly called for. The gunpowder must be seized. The Americans must be soothed or coaxed out of their decision not to import British goods. The steps were agreed upon, and the governors of those colonies where gunpowder was suspected to be stored were ordered to seize it.

In Virginia, the haughty, fiery Lord Dunmore moved into action. He had been off in the western frontier of Virginia on that tour on which George Washington was to have accompanied him. It was something more than a tour. It was a campaign of conquest in which, with the aid of frontiersmen, Dunmore had subdued the Indians and concluded a peace with the Shawnee who had been on the warpath.

That peace was to benefit greatly Virginia in the years ahead, and Dunmore had conducted himself with courage and wisdom among the Indians. He brought none of it back to Williamsburg. He seized fifteen barrels of gunpowder belonging to the colonists which were stored in the magazine in Williamsburg and transferred them to the man-of-war *Fowey* at anchor twelve miles down the York River. In Massachusetts Governor Gage attempted the same thing, sending his redcoats to Lexington and Concord.

When news reached the people that the gunpowder in Williamsburg had been seized there was a roaring reaction in Virginia. Angry crowds gathered outside the Governor's mansion, flinging stones into the grounds. Marines from the *Fowey* had to be brought to secure the Governor's safety. All over Virginia the militia began to arm. Then, through the Committee of Correspondence, came the report of the battles of Lexington and Concord, and the bloody retreat of the British into their stronghold at Boston.

In the north, the war had already started. Virginians were not going to lag behind the men of Massachusetts. Patrick Henry organized a body of militia in Hanover County and began a march on Williamsburg to demand the return of the confiscated powder. Dunmore heard he was coming—and Dunmore feared Henry. He sent an agent out to meet him with money to pay for the powder, and for the moment the crisis passed.

Tom Jefferson arrived in Williamsburg to find the town in a turmoil, everyone talking of the battles of Lexington and Concord and half the people in hunting shirts and armed with rifles. Even gentle George Wythe, too old a man to fight, bought himself a hunting shirt and turned from the study of his lawyer's briefs to learning how to charge and prime a musket. But Jefferson carried no rifle and wore no hunting shirt.

"Where are your arms?" his friends asked him.

Jefferson glanced at a quill pen on his desk but said nothing.

Finding the whole of Virginia in arms against him, Governor Dunmore summoned a meeting of the House of Burgesses. He had received instructions from Lord North, the British Prime Minister, to offer conciliatory terms.

"I have called you together," said Governor Dunmore, "to give you an opportunity of taking the alarming state of the colony into your consideration, and providing remedies against the evils which are increasing therein."

There were some grim chuckles from the Burgesses at these words. The message was all conciliation, informing the Burgesses that their "well-founded grievances, properly represented, will meet with the attention and regard which are so justly due them," and that, regarding taxation, "no specific sum is demanded of you . . . that your justice and liberality may be left full scope and that your gift, if you should be induced to offer any, may be in the most completest manner, free."

"Properly represented," Patrick Henry grunted to Jefferson. "By thunder, the only time that pack of rascals listen to us is when our grievances are improperly represented—not by sweet petitions but by musket balls."

"We'll have to make a reply," said Jefferson.

"Agreed," said Henry. "And so long as the good Mr. Nicholas hasn't anything to do with it, it will leave Governor Dunmore and the King of England with no doubts about our attitude."

Tom smiled. The elderly, grave Mr. Nicholas was one of the leaders of the conciliatory faction. Firm in his principles of freedom, he still believed freedom would best be served by soft words and phrases. "We'll see," he said.

Peyton Randolph, Speaker of the House of Burgesses, had been attending the meeting of the Second Continental Congress, in session at Philadelphia. The members of the Second Continental Congress knew of the conciliatory offer now being made by Lord North through the various colonial governors. They knew of them and thought them contemptuous. But Peyton Randolph was worried that in his absence from Williamsburg, Mr. Nicholas would be given the job of drafting Virginia's reply to the offer. He hurried back to Williamsburg from Philadelphia and sought out Tom Jefferson.

"Tom," he said, "you will have to draft our reply. If Mr. Nicholas handles it, the reply will be too soft. He has spent so many years as a loyal subject of the King that he can never screw himself up to defiance—to a bold demand for our rights."

"How long can you give me?" asked Tom.

"A day. Two at the outside. Our reply must reach the Continental Congress at the earliest moment. It is vital that it should be strong. If it looks as though Virginia is wavering, the effect on the other colonies would be disastrous."

"You will have the reply in two days," said Tom. A committee to draft a reply had been appointed. Tom talked with the members, got their views, and went to his writing desk in his lodgings.

Meanwhile the turmoil in the town had increased. The House of Burgesses had decided to inquire into the Governor's right to seize the barrels of gunpowder. Three men entered the arsenal to see what powder remained. They were wounded by a gun trap Dunmore had placed there. The town was outraged by the wounding of the men and ready for revenge. Armed men gathered around the mansion shouting insults at the Governor. Dunmore lost his nerve and on the night of June 8, fled with his family to the safety of the man-of-war *Fowey*.

The Governor's flight ended British rule in Virginia. In fact, British rule had ended in two colonies, though few realized it at the time. Dunmore had sought refuge on a battleship and General Gage, Governor of Massachusetts, was locked up in Boston, though he expected shortly, when he got more soldiers from England, to break out.

Tom Jefferson had his reply to Lord North's conciliatory proposal ready in two days, as promised. The reply was firm, well reasoned and courageous. It said the proposal could not be accepted and listed the reasons:

The British Parliament had no right to meddle with the government of the colonies.

The British government was asking a grant of money while insisting it had the right to levy taxes on the colonies. No grant of money could be made while Britain still insisted on the right to tax Americans without representation.

The British government while asking for a grant was preparing to invade the colonies having sent ships and men for that purpose, "a style of asking gifts not reconcilable to our freedom . . ."

If the colonies contributed money to the common defense of the British empire, they should be allowed freedom of trade with any country in the world. But Britain still denied the colonies freedom of trade.

In any case, the proposition made to Virginians affected all the colonies. They were united now in a Congress of their own. Virginia was bound in honor and interest to share the fate of her sister colonies and would not desert the union with them. A full reply could then only come from all thirteen colonies.

The final paragraphs were masterly.

We have exhausted every mode of application which our invention could suggest as proper and promising [Jefferson wrote]. We have decently remonstrated with Parliament; they have added new injuries to old. We have wearied our King with supplications; he has not deigned to answer us. We have appealed to the native honour and justice of the British nation; their efforts in our favour have hitherto been ineffectual.

The case was clear. There would be no more supplications and no reconciliation until Britain renounced the right to tax her American colonies.

Jefferson and Peyton Randolph obtained the approval of the Virginia convention to this reply and then Tom set out with a copy of it for Philadelphia to present it to the Congress to which he was an alternate delegate with Peyton Randolph.

He traveled by phaeton, a light two-wheeled carriage; but though he was in a hurry, he had time to make notes of the flora and fauna of Maryland, to visit the State House at Annapolis, and to buy some books.

In Fredericksburg he bought a horse—a magnificent animal named General which was to become his favorite. His journey took him a week, for roads were poor and in some places nothing more than a trace. In Philadelphia he took lodgings with a cabinet-maker, Benjamin Randolph, and found himself, with his entry into the city, suddenly on the world stage.

Tremendous events had taken place while Tom Jefferson was on his way to Philadelphia. A whole government had been set up, deriving its powers from the Congress, and with the authority to make war, conclude peace and enter into alliances with other nations. The issuance of three million dollars in paper currency was authorized. Provision was made for the formation of a regular army, for the enlistment of men and the construction of forts.

In a matter of a few weeks the whole character of America was changed and British rule had gone. And yet no formal renunciation of Britain had been made, and many still hung back from it. Men still drank the

King's health at dinner and "perdition to the King's enemies." They did not think of themselves as the King's enemies. They were his loyal subjects, demanding rights due to them and of which the King himself was unaware had been taken from them by conniving ministers. So the people believed.

A big problem had arisen concerning the New England militiamen who, under the leadership of Artemus Ward, now hemmed in the British garrison and General Gage in Boston.

Patrick Henry told Jefferson, when he arrived, what had taken place. "Some delegates were against adopting the New England army," he said. "Others said if it wasn't adopted by the Congress it would dissolve and Gage would come bursting out of Boston and lay waste to the whole countryside. Then there was the question of a general if the Congress decided to adopt the army. Artemus Ward held command. But many members thought John Hancock should be given command. The southern colonies didn't like the idea of a New England army commanded by a New England general.

"John Adams solved the problem. He moved that the Congress officially adopt the Army as the Continental Army and appoint a general. He went further than that. He said that there was one man from Virginia sitting among them whose skill and experience and talents eminently fitted him for the post of General . . ."

"Washington?" asked Tom.

"Right," said Patrick Henry. "Washington was sitting by the door—in the background as usual. You know how he hates to speak in public or look as if he's putting himself forward. As soon as he suspected that Adams was talking about him, his face went scarlet and he sneaked out into the library. I've never seen a man so embarrassed in my life.

"Well, that's the way it went. The army is the Continental Army and Washington is the General—a big tribute to Virginia as well as to him, I might add."

"And a very astute move by Mr. Adams," said Tom. "For now no one can complain. The army may be from New England, but the commander is a southerner—and at the same time the best soldier in all the colonies."

One of the first men Tom Jefferson met in Philadelphia was Dr. Benjamin Franklin, then sixty-nine years of age, and newly returned from London where he had been agent for the colonies pleading the American cause but without success. They talked of the crucial issue of the break with the King which seemed to be more and more imminent.

"Sir," said Franklin in his quiet, good humored voice, that still bore traces of a New England accent though he had lived in Philadelphia and London most of his life, "as you know, people have risen against kings before. In England there was the great rebellion against Charles I who was subsequently beheaded. One of the men who signed the papers authorizing the execution of the King made a statement which, I fancy, applies to us now."

"What statement was that?" asked Jefferson.

"'Rebellion to tyrants is obedience to God,'" replied Franklin.

"'Rebellion to tyrants is obedience to God,'" repeated Tom Jefferson. The words seemed to sum up everything in which he believed. Years later when he designed a signet ring for himself, the sentence was incorporated in the design, summarizing his deepest belief.

Jefferson took his seat in the Congress as soon as he arrived, and when he rose to present Virginia's reply to Lord North's proposals, all heads turned to see him. The greatest men in the colonies were present—John Adams and his second cousin Sam Adams; John Hancock; Benjamin Franklin; John Dickinson, the most revered man in Philadelphia; Edward Rutledge of South Carolina; and George Read of Delaware. These men had all read Tom Jefferson's "A Summary View of the Rights of British America" and agreed with every word. They rose in their seats straining to see the author. Jefferson made a good impression as he stood among them—tall, angular, decently but not foppishly dressed, his face tanned, his voice quiet but firm.

"These Virginians," one delegate said to his neighbor. "They seem to be a special breed."

"From what I hear of Jefferson, he is special even among the Virginians," said the other.

"A fighting man, eh?"

"A lover of liberty," was the reply. "The best horseman in Virginia, I hear. And the best penman too."

After receiving permission from the Speaker, John Hancock, Jefferson read Virginia's reply to Lord North's proposal—calmly, without heroics. The very quietness of his voice lent force to the words. When he was done the delegates cheered. Virginia had given the reply Congress wanted to hear and that Congress itself was about to give on behalf of all the colonies.

But not all were in favor of so bold an answer. Pennsylvania, led by John Dickinson, was not ready for a break, not ready yet for strong frank words demanding American rights.

The southern and northern colonies were ripe for an end to British meddling of any kind in American affairs. The central colonies, led by Dickinson, held that Britain's Parliament had the right to pass laws regulating the trade of the colonies, and, provided taxes levied were for the purpose of controlling trade and not for the purpose of raising revenue, the colonies should submit.

There was also a curious unshakable loyalty towards the person of the King which irritated Jefferson, Patrick Henry and Richard Henry Lee. Yet it was there, this belief that the King did not know how badly his subjects in the American colonies were being treated, that he was totally misled by his ministers.

Ben Franklin did not share this belief. He had spent many years in England, where he had been admired by the people and disliked by the court. He knew that the King's ministers were the tools of the King. But he was wise enough to let others find out for themselves.

Franklin was chosen to head a committee to draft a reply to Lord North's proposals. And Tom Jefferson, newly arrived in Philadelphia, came next in the number of votes cast for membership in the committee. Hardly had the committee been chosen than a dust-covered rider from New England clattered into Philadelphia on a sweat-lathered horse with the news of the Battle of Bunker Hill.

"We licked the redcoats!" he shouted. "We gave them a drubbing they'll not forget. There was a pitched battle and we'd have beaten them thoroughly if we had not run out of powder."

The whole town was in a furor at the news. The militia paraded through the streets to celebrate. Groups of men, some with and some without leaders, marched off with their muskets to swell the army outside Boston. This was war—real war. There was no room left now for negotiations, and the time for polite petitions, nicely worded to avoid offense, was long past.

Jefferson was appointed to draft the reply to Lord North's proposals and did so. He used the reply which he had written for the Virginia House of Burgesses for his model, and the words came out clean and hot as cannon shot. And yet, despite Lexington and Concord and Bunker Hill, the middle colonies, led by Dickin-

son, insisted that the fire be taken out of the reply—
that the ardor be subdued and the phrases more politely couched.

Tom Jefferson was also given the job, together with
John Dickinson of Philadelphia, of drafting an address for Washington to deliver to the army, setting
forth the reasons why they had taken up arms. He
went at it with vigor, for the reasons were perfectly
clear to him. But Dickinson would not agree to so
bold a statement and in deference to him the draft
was watered down.

"Dear God," cried Jefferson. "How long must we
obscure the whole issue in polite phrases when what
is wanted is common frankness?"

"Bah," cried John Adams. "That Dickinson has a
fiddling kind of genius. He fears to offend with as
much as a misplaced comma. But the time for correspondence is long past. The issue will be settled
only by musket balls."

"You were never more right in your life, sir," said
Patrick Henry.

Having adopted the army, appointed Washington
its commander, set rules for the pay and enlistment
of men and approved its reply to Lord North's proposals, the Congress, after a very lengthy session going on into winter, adjourned and Tom Jefferson returned home to Monticello.

He was, in all things, a man of reason, slow to anger. But as week after week went by and there was no

sign of a relenting in the attitude of Britain, no reply
to the message of the Continental Congress to Lord
North in London, his blood began to boil. Unlike Patrick Henry, Tom Jefferson rarely spoke his anger. He
wrote it. And when his relative, John Randolph, who
was pro-British, decided to leave the colonies for
England, since he disagreed with the colonial re-
sistance to the King's armies, Tom wrote him a letter.
He liked John Randolph and respected him, but, at
the risk of shattering their friendship, he stated his
mind clearly.

". . . there is not in the British empire a man who
would more cordially love a union with Great Britain
than I do," he wrote. "But by the God that made me,
I will cease to exist before I yield to a connection on
such terms as the British Parliament propose, and in
this I think I speak the sentiments of America. We
want neither inducement nor power to declare and
assert a separation . . . we must drub him [General
Howe who had now replaced Gage] soundly, before
the sceptred tyrant will know we are not mere
brutes, to crouch under his hand, and kiss the rod
with which he deigns to scourge us."

Jefferson's mind through the spring of 1776 was
greatly troubled. Many things were clear. Some
things were unclear. It was clear to him that no settlement with Britain was possible without agreement
on the principle of no taxation without representation; clear to him that every American had the rights

granted freely to every Englishman; clear that the British Parliament had no right to overrule the laws passed by the colonial legislatures.

But he had been all his life a British subject: a Virginian, an American—and British. To part with the people whose blood he shared—to part with traditions which were his traditions; to part with that whole body of law which provided more justice for a man in court than was available anywhere else in the world—that was a hard thing to do.

George Washington's estate, Mount Vernon, was named after an English admiral who had been a friend of Washington's father. Jefferson's old home, Shadwell, had been named after a London parish. There were a thousand thin but strong ties like these that bound him emotionally to Britain. Were they now to be cut and England hereafter to be a foreign and hated nation?

He spent the period until the next and third session of the Continental Congress, as did many other prominent Americans, in an agony of mind; firm in his principles, determined that there should be no surrender of rights, but hoping that somehow, in some way, a settlement would be found.

Meanwhile, outside Boston, the Continental Army huddled in rude huts in the bitter cold, besieging the redcoats. They called the army opposing them not the King's army but the Ministerial army. The King was the protector and father of his people. The officers drank his health every night at dinner, George

Washington himself proposing the toast. The King's scheming ministers alone were the enemy.

In Philadelphia, in a cheap lodginghouse, was a man newly arrived from England, who took another view of the King. He called the King not father but tyrant; not protector but "royal brute." Working by the light of a penny candle, he was writing a pamphlet that was to shake all America.

His name was Thomas Paine, and the pamphlet he wrote was titled *Common Sense.*

☆ ☆ ☆ ☆ ☆ ☆ ☆ ☆ ☆ ☆ ☆ ☆

14

The year 1776 was ushered in by the bombardment of Norfolk, Virginia, by British ships, the order for the attack being given by Lord Dunmore. The man who only two or three years before had held court in Williamsburg, establishing an order of precedence for the seating of prominent Virginians at his table; who had frequently invited George Washington to dine with him, and had asked Tom Jefferson to draw up plans for improving William and Mary College—this man now broke out his true colors.

He declared Virginia in a state of revolt and placed it under martial law. Then he invited the slaves to join him in a revolt against their masters. Finally he ordered the British ships to open fire on Norfolk and after a bombardment of three days, the whole town was destroyed with the exception of St. Paul's Church.

Previously Dunmore had ordered raids by British sailors along the Virginia coast, so that the war, which had so far been confined to Massachusetts, now flared up in Virginia. Tom Jefferson had news of these events before he left Philadelphia to return to Monticello. He was on his way back when Norfolk was burned to the ground. The whole colony was in a turmoil.

His friend John Page was worried that his plantation in the Tidewater section would be razed. Another friend, Thomas Nelson, begged Jefferson to bring his family from Monticello to Philadelphia, where they would be safe. A major assault by the British under Dunmore up the James River was expected. But for Jefferson Monticello was the dearest place on earth. He would not leave it. He stayed there, and in all the torment of mind in which he was now placed, he went ahead with the building of his lovely mansion, taking care of his numerous family.

All seemed very dark to Tom Jefferson in those days. His kinsman Peyton Randolph had died of apoplexy in October, 1775. His wife was in poor health. In March, 1776, his mother, living with him at Monticello, died. Jefferson himself, overwrought by public worries and private grief, became ill, suffering from piercing headaches which would give him no peace. To regain some serenity he went walking or riding in the woods around his estate, trying to get from the nature he loved the strength he would need for the terrible days he sensed loomed ahead.

He loved Virginia and would always love it. He was anguished by the brutalities Dunmore was inflicting on the land, but powerless to do anything to prevent them. In these terrible times a new kind of strength developed in him—the strength to endure in silence and patience every kind of hardship. Gentle and reasonable by nature, he developed a rocklike fortitude, so that in future, misfortune, public or private, might hurt him, but would not conquer him.

Jefferson had hardly returned from Philadelphia when his friend Thomas Nelson sent him a letter.

"I am sending to you a present of two shillings worth of Common Sense," wrote Nelson, enclosing the pamphlet written by Thomas Paine. Jefferson read it at one sitting and his spirits soared.

Here was the clear voice of courage cutting through all the confusion of quibbling doubts and anxious compromise. One man, a corsetmaker, dared to unmask the King on his throne and show him for what he was—a tyrant and a brute, unworthy to rule; a coarse, low, bloody-minded dictator bent upon the enslavement rather than the protection of his people.

Paine's pamphlet Common Sense was like the trumpet call preceding battle. It swept aside the last lingering doubts of Americans in taking up arms against their King; pointed to him as the enemy and charged them to throw off his rule. Others might have secretly harbored the same thoughts about the King, but the shadow of the noose prevented their committing them to paper. Paine spoke out—spoke out hot and sharp, putting aside all fears and pretenses.

Paine denounced George III as a "hardened sullen-tempered Pharaoh" and "the Royal Brute of Great Britain." He demolished the pretense to which Americans still clung that there was a difference between the King and his ministers and between the King and his Parliament. Ministers and Parliament were the tools of the King, and the King a tyrant. As a tyrant, his rule must be overthrown by force of arms. America must declare itself independent of King, Lords and Commons, and sustain that independence with her blood. That was the only course available to free men.

This was the conclusion to which Jefferson himself had already come, even before Paine published *Common Sense*. His heart ached at the thought of breaking the old ties with England. But he knew they must be broken, and he had not been deceived into thinking the King the friend of Americans, deceived by his own ministers.

Independence, then—independence achieved by sword, musket, and cannon—that was the answer. But the independence must be declared. It must be made clear to the world that this was no mere colonial revolt arising out of anger over taxes on sugar and tea. Far larger issues were at stake—issues bearing on the relationship of men to any government they might have over them. The time had come to set down on paper that great charter of natural rights Tom Jefferson had talked about so much with George Wythe—those rights which he believed in the depth of his soul must never be taken from men by any government, any police agency, any court of law.

In May 1776, Tom Jefferson set out for the meeting of the Third Continental Congress in Philadelphia. He was pale from his illness and concerned about his wife who was still not well. Yet on larger matters, his mind was at ease at last, for he knew what was to be done, and knew also that the time had come for doing it.

When he arrived in Philadelphia Tom Jefferson found that others were of the same conviction. Tom Paine's pamphlet had worked a magic on men, settling their last doubts about taking the grave step over which they had previously hesitated.

"What of Washington?" Jefferson asked John Adams when they met in Philadelphia.

"He's tired of artful declarations and pretenses," said Adams. "He asks for open, undisguised, manly terms proclaiming our wrongs and our resolution to be redressed."

"Independence?" Jefferson asked.

Adams nodded. "Independence," he said. "It is a flame. South Carolina and North Carolina are for it. Virginia surely will not lag behind."

Jefferson smiled. He knew Virginia would be in the forefront for independence, and indeed soon had news that the Virginia Convention meeting in Williamsburg had voted to instruct its delegates to the Continental Congress to propose "to declare the United Colonies free and independent States, absolved from all allegiance to, or dependence on, the Crown or Parliament of Great Britain."

On June 7, 1776, Richard Henry Lee, delegate to the Congress with Tom Jefferson, rose and presented Virginia's resolution calling for independence. "The resolution of Virginia, sir, is as follows," he said to the Speaker. "Resolved that these United Colonies are, and of right ought to be, free and independent States, that they are absolved from all allegiance to the British Crown, and that all political connection between them and the State of Great Britain is and ought to be, totally dissolved."

John Adams rose to second the resolution—north and south were united—Virginia and Massachusetts. Suddenly there was an uproar. Shouts of "Liberty!" and "Long live Virginia!" filled the hall. The turmoil lasted several minutes, delegates climbing over chairs to shake the hands of Lee and Adams.

But when the outburst quieted down, it was found that not all the colonies were prepared to support the resolution. Pennsylvania held back and so did New York and Maryland. There was a long debate, lasting until seven that evening and continuing the following day.

Tom Jefferson took no part in the debate. Some hotly supported the resolution of independence; others supported it but said the time was not ripe. Others were opposed to the break with the mother country. Jefferson was not angry. He did not demand that all men share his convictions. He demanded only that they state their reasons for thinking otherwise and was anxious to investigate these reasons with them.

June 8 was a Saturday. The Congress debated through the whole day, and finally decided to postpone the vote on Virginia's resolution calling for independence until July 1. That would give the hesitant delegates time to think the matter over and get in touch with their own people back home.

Meanwhile a committee was appointed to draw up a declaration of independence, should the colonies later agree to the break. The committee consisted of Thomas Jefferson, Benjamin Franklin, John Adams, Roger Sherman, and R. R. Livingston. Francis Hopkinson of New Jersey was added a little later to the committee.

A document may be agreed to by a committee. But it must be written by one man. There was no disagreement over who should write the declaration. The job was assigned to Tom Jefferson. On arrival in Philadelphia, he had taken rooms in a new brick house on the corner of Market and Seventh streets. The house belonged to a bricklayer named Graff who was newly married. Tom Jefferson's rooms were on the second floor, and consisted of a bedroom and parlor.

He had had a folding writing box made for him and he opened it and put it on a table in the parlor. He had no books with him and no reference sources, for he had no need of them now. What he was about to write had long been in his mind. In the silence of the room, alone, with several blank sheets of paper before him, he paused to collect his thoughts— thoughts of the slaves who had asked him on his father's death to whom they belonged, of Patrick Henry's great cry, "Give me liberty or give me death," of Richard Henry Lee's resolution that the united colonies ought to be free, of the petitions written to the King's ministers and to the King, and of the men he had seen in Virginia and Philadelphia marching with firelocks and muskets to join the army in Boston.

The whole panorama unfolded in his mind—the arguments about natural rights, the writings of Locke and Montesquieu and Ferguson. And then the friend who, holding a musket, had asked him why he was unarmed.

Calmly Tom Jefferson reached for a quill pen, took out a pocket knife, and trimmed the point. The action was similar to the priming of a musket. He dipped the pen in his inkwell and started to write.

"When in the course of human events it becomes necessary for one people to dissolve the political bands which have connected them with another . . ."

The words came to him readily. Like the explosion

of the musket at Lexington shattering the silence of the day, they were to be heard around the world, echoing and re-echoing; never to die—speaking of freedom from tyranny for all men everywhere.

END OF THE FIRST VOLUME

AUTHOR'S NOTE

If you will go to your public library—and I hope you will—and look at the card index under JEFFERSON, THOMAS, you will find a highway of cards traveling off into the distance of the drawer, each one of them cataloguing a book about the man who was given the job of drafting the Declaration of Independence. There is then no need for me to include in this book a bibliography on Thomas Jefferson. Any library has lots of books on Jefferson in all his phases; philosopher, inventor, architect, agriculturalist, musician, traveler, diplomat, President of the United States; whatever the aspect of his career, there is a multitude of books on the subject.

The books I used were got from the public library, but in my reading of perhaps twenty books on the youth of Jefferson, I discovered something very curious. At the end of the reading, what came out was a figure but not a human being. Jefferson was so great a man, so vast in his accomplishments and so advanced in his education, that he suffers even in the hands of the most loving biographers from a lack of humanity.

Another curious discovery arising from my reading of books on Jefferson is the tendency of many authors to divorce him utterly from his times. One volume gave every possible detail of his life—how much he paid for the shoeing of a horse, how much he paid to cross a ferry, where he bought a thermometer, and so on. But the author had nothing to say about the effect on Jefferson of the collapse of the French in the New World after the Battle of Abraham Heights. That was an overwhelmingly important event for British Americans, removing the French military threat to their existence and indeed making possible the Revolution which was to follow. It was tremendous good news for Jefferson. Yet author after author writes of him as if Jefferson lived in a cloister and had never heard this or other staggering news of his day. Suddenly he is there, pulled out of the law practice and the House of Burgesses, writing the Declaration of Independence. It certainly didn't happen that way.

The best all-round book, essential to a knowledge of Jefferson and his times, is, in my opinion, *Origins of the American Revolution* by John C. Miller (Atlantic-Little, Brown). There isn't much of Jefferson in it; only a mention or two. But to understand Jefferson as anything but a pedant who, surprisingly, wrote the famous Declaration, it is essential to understand his times. *Origins of the American Revolution* is the best introduction to them.

Jefferson in his later years wrote a brief autobiography, but he was no Walpole. He did not write intimately about himself, and so his autobiography is only a summary of the main events of the first two thirds of his life. But coming from such a mind and hand it is well worth reading, and there are revealing little glimpses of Jefferson, the man, to be seen through the Augustan prose of the eighteenth century.

Marie Gould Kimball's *Jefferson—The Road to Glory,* is a carefully researched volume on Jefferson's youth. It reads, I am sorry to say, a bit like a treatise for a college degree in many places. Yet it is a most valuable volume containing a mass of information on Jefferson's early years.

Other books I found valuable were *Thomas Jefferson* by William Eleroy Curtis and *Life and Writings of Thomas Jefferson* by Samuel Eagle Forman. There are indeed a host of books on Jefferson; and I even found the neglected *Life and Times of Washington* by Washington Irving not only pleasant reading, but full of anecdotal detail which is the lifeblood of any book.

I hope no one is going to take this book as one of learning. I have been at pains to be accurate and have not consciously put down any inaccuracy concerning Thomas Jefferson.

But I am a novelist and have had to imagine the talks between him and Patrick Henry and Dabney Carr and his other friends. They are recorded nowhere. Even if they had been recorded, it would probably have been in the stilted fashion of the eighteenth century and thus not much more accurate than my own imaginings and deductions.

This, then, is a novelist's story of Jefferson. He would not have liked it, for he thought novels a waste of time and tried to restrict his reading to nonfiction. Yet he fell in love with a piece of fiction which he thought fact—some writing about Ossian, the mythological Celtic figure, issued as though they were translations of the work of the legendary poet. He wanted to study Celtic to read them in the original, regarded them as sublime, and thoroughly believed in their authenticity.

So we novelists have our little revenge, and Jefferson, the nonfiction lover tricked by fiction, proves quite as human as modern readers who will devour any kind of nonsense provided it is labeled nonfiction.

I personally bridge the gap. This book is nonfiction

fiction. Let my friends the librarians puzzle over the classification. For the reader, I hope only that he enjoys it.

Leonard Wibberley

Hermosa Beach,
California.

INDEX